PLANTS AND FLOWERS

of

MALAYSIA

© **1988 Times Editions Pte Ltd**
Reprinted 1991, 1992, 1994

Times Editions Pte Ltd
Times Centre
1 New Industrial Road
Singapore 1953

Times Subang
Lot 46, Subang Hi-Tech Industrial Park
Batu Tiga
40000 Shah Alam
Selangor Darul Ehsan
Malaysia

Printed in Singapore.

ISBN 981 204 021 8

PLANTS AND FLOWERS
of
MALAYSIA

IVAN POLUNIN

TIMES EDITIONS

Contents

THE PLANTS IN THEIR SETTING

This book aims to give a brief and elementary account of the natural vegetation of Malaysia, both in its original and its present state, and of some of the species of plant of which this vegetation is composed.

In a book of this size, it is only possible to present about two per cent of Malaysia's native or naturalized flowering plants. So a somewhat arbitrary sampling of the important, the common, the beautiful and the interesting species is given here. Forest trees with their inaccessible fruits and flowers, the generally less attractive weeds and grasses, and non-flowering plants are under-represented, while some cultivated plants native to South, East and Southeast Asia have been included.

BACKGROUND

Malaysia is divided into two main parts: Peninsular Malaysia, and the contiguous states of Sabah and Sarawak, which occupy most of the northern coast of the island of Borneo. The two parts of Malaysia are separated by about 600 kilometres of shallow water.

Above the famous waterfall at Lombong, Kota Tinggi, is this remnant of the forest that once covered the Malay Peninsula. On the left is the stemless palm Eugeissona tristis,*the Bertam,whose leaflets are used by forest-dwellers for* atap *roofing.*

Only about 10,000 years ago, during the last ice age, the Malay Peninsula and Borneo were connected by dry land. This is a mere moment ago in geological time, and the interval since then represents perhaps one ten-thousandth part of the period during which there have been flowering plants on earth. As most plants can easily spread overland by natural means, and as conditions in both parts of Malaysia are similar, we would expect that the two floras resemble each other, and in fact 90 per cent of tree species native to Peninsular Malaysia are also native to Borneo and Sumatera. Brunei Darussalam, being surrounded by Sarawak, has physical conditions and vegetation similar to that of eastern Sarawak.

CLIMATE

The climate of Malaysia is ever-wet tropical: the annual rainfall is high, averaging 221 centimetres for Melaka to 390 centimetres in Kuching, with higher rainfall in some parts of the mountainous interior of Sarawak. This rainfall is distributed in such a way that there is no regular dry period to interfere seriously with the survival or even the growth of plants, because the soil is nearly always sufficiently moist. This does not mean that the rain is evenly distributed; in fact the most marked seasonal variations of climate are in the rainfall, due to the northeast monsoon at the turn of the year and the southwest monsoon in mid-year.

There is quite a considerable variation from the average, with places experiencing irregular month-long dry periods. Only in the northwest corner of the Malay Peninsula, west of a line running from Alur Setar to Songkhla in Thailand, is there a definite dry season sufficiently severe to turn the grass brown and cause many trees to drop their leaves. This marks the climatic boundary between ever-wet Malaysia and monsoonal Thailand. It is also an important botanical border which 375 Malaysian and 200 Thai genera of flowering plants do not cross.

NATIVE, NATURALIZED AND CULTIVATED PLANTS

The great majority of plant species growing wild in Malaysia are natives, but some plants brought in by human agency have run wild, and have become naturalized. These are mainly short-lived weeds of cultivation and some introduced as ornamentals but have since run wild, for instance Water Hyacinth (p.80) and *Lantana camara* (*Tahi Ayam*). These, together with *Eupatorium odoratum* (*Lupang*) and Mile-a-minute (p.46), have reached plague proportions in some places, probably because of a lack of natural enemies, which kept them in check in their native habitat.

Most of the cultivated plants in Malaysia were introduced from abroad. This is not surprising because Malaysia has less than five per cent of the world's flowering plant species.*

---

* Dr Hsuan Keng in the *Journal of Tropical Geography* (1963, v.28, p.43) estimated between 8,000 to 8,500 species of flowering plants to be natives of the Malay Peninsula. The world total probably lies between 215,000 and 250,000 species. An educated guess for Malaysia would be 10,000 species.

We cannot be certain that Malaysia is *the* country of origin of any one cultivated plant, except where orchids collected in Malaysia have become the parents of a hybrid. This is because most plants which are native to Malaysia are also native to one or more of its neighbouring countries such as Thailand, Indonesia or the Philippines, and many cultivated plants are unknown in the wild state.

Malaysia and its neighbours are, however, an important centre of origin of fruit trees. Thus several genera have more than one species which are native Malaysian fruit trees. These include *Artocarpus* (*Cempedak, Terap*), *Baccaurea* (*Tampoi* spp., *Rambai*), *Citrus* (limes, Pomelo), *Durio* (Durians), *Eugenia* (*Jambu Air* and *Jambu Bol*, p.140), *Garcinia* (Mangosteen, *Gelugur*), *Mangifera* (*Binjai, Bambangan*) and *Nephelium* (*Rambutan, Mata Kucing*). With the diversity of trees in the forest, who knows what fruit trees and other potentially useful plants are to be found there, their usefulness still unrecognized?

VEGETATION AND WHAT INFLUENCES IT

The plant life in an area grows in communities, which constitute the vegetation. Each species has its own life history and growth form, its own set of environmental requirements and interrelations with other species, including animals. Generally speaking, the more favourable the conditions are for plant life, the larger the number of species comprising the vegetation, while paucity of species suggests unfavourable conditions. Thus at one end we find the species-rich lowland rainforest, while at the other we find the pioneers of the mangrove edge or the sandy beach, where only a few hardy and well-adapted species can survive.

Natural circumstances which influence vegetation are altitude, which affects temperature and rainfall, soil type, land relief and drainage, wind exposure and salinity. Many of these act by determining the water conditions in the soil.

In Malaysia, altitude is the only factor which is responsible for large differences in temperature from place to place, and temperature is probably responsible for the mountain and lowland species being almost entirely different. Its importance is shown by the fact that there are very few species native both to Malaysia and the cold regions directly to the north. Malaysian plants are killed by the cold; similarly, most plants from temperate or cold climates will not thrive in Malaysia, though some of them will grow better in the mountains, making possible Malaysia's highland vegetable and cut-flower industry. Exceptional examples of plants which grow in temperate Europe as well as lowland Malaysia are the Bracken Fern (*Pteridium aquilinum*), the little Yellow Wood Sorrel (*Oxalis corniculata*), the Bulrush (*Typha angustifolia*) and Bermuda Grass (*Cynodon dactylon*). Even among these the temperate and tropical plants probably have genetic differences in temperature tolerance.

The effect of rainfall is easy to appreciate when a desert is compared with a rainforest. Both the species of plants and their physical characteristics are utterly different, as is the structure of the vegetation. Malaysian plants thrive under ever-wet conditions and are poorly able to withstand dry periods as they receive at least ten centimetres of rain a month. This kind of climate is almost confined to parts of Southeast Asia. The rainforests of Africa and even those of large parts of Amazonia have a distinct dry season.

Vegetation itself is an important determinant of what grows. This is clearly shown on the forest floor where all plants must be able to tolerate the deep shade produced by the trees. Up in the trees, the bark of trunks and branches becomes a perch for epiphytes such as orchids, ferns and lichens, and in the most humid places, even the leathery, long-lived leaves of forest trees and shrubs may be covered by a growth of micro-epiphytes, algae, lichens and mosses (illustrated on p.31).

MAJOR FAMILIES OF MALAYSIAN PLANTS

Related groups of native plants which are richly represented in Malaysia include the Orchid family (Orchidaceae) with up to 2,000 species, mostly epiphytes, and Dipterocarpaceae, the Dipterocarp family, with several hundred species, which reaches its greatest diversity in Borneo. There are also at least 220 species of palm (Arecaceae or Palmae) in the Peninsula, over five times the number native to the whole of Africa: of these 104 are climbing palms, the Rattans. The Myrtle family (Myrtaceae) has about 150 species of *Eugenia* in the Peninsula, most of which are endemics, but none of the closely related *Eucalyptus*. The Ginger family (Zingiberaceae) has more than 150 species in Peninsular Malaysia, mostly large herbs. *Nepenthes*, which belongs to the small family Nepenthaceae, one of three families of carnivorous Pitcher Plants in the world, has about 30 species, nearly half the world's total.

Among non-flowering plants, there are about 500 species of fern in the Peninsula, about five per cent of the world's total: they are an important part of the forest undergrowth, as most ferns need a damp and shady environment. Others are epiphytes.

We will now look briefly at the main types of natural vegetation in Malaysia which could be encountered on a journey from the low tidemark up to the shore, and from the lowlands to the highlands, before touching on vegetation modified by man.

MALAYSIA: VEGETATION AND CLIMATE

Songkhla

THAILAND

PERLIS
Kangar

Pulau Langkawi

Alur Setar

KEDAH

Gunung
Jerai

Kota Bahru

SOUTH CHINA SEA

Georgetown
PINANG

PERAK

KELANTAN

Kuala Terengganu

TERENGGANU

Taiping
Kuala Kangsar

Ipoh

Gunung
Berincang
2031

Cameron
Highlands

Kuala Lipis

6

Bukit
Fraser

PAHANG

Kuantan

SELANGOR

Gunung
Ulu Kali

Batu Caves
Petaling Jaya

Kuala Lumpur

Tasek Cini

Tasek Bera

NEGERI
SEMBILAN

Seremban

Rompin

Endau

Mersing

MELAKA

JOHOR

Sungei Sedili

Melaka

Air Hitam

Gunung
Panti

Kuala Sedili Besar

Teluk Makhota

SUMATERA

Lombong

Kota Tinggi

Johor Bahru

SINGAPORE

Scale
0   100   200 km

Climate

temperature:
—— max. mean (°C)
- - - min. mean (°C)
(500) annual rainfall (mm.)

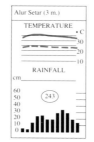

Alur Setar (3 m.)

TEMPERATURE
•C
30
20
10

RAINFALL

cm
60
50
40
30
20
10
0

243

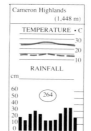

Cameron Highlands
(1,448 m.)

TEMPERATURE •C
30
20
10

RAINFALL

cm
60
50
40
30
20
10
0

264

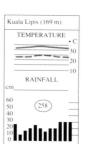

Kuala Lipis (169 m.)

TEMPERATURE
•C
30
20
10

RAINFALL

cm
60
50
40
30
20
10
0

258

Kuala Lumpur (39 m.)

TEMPERATURE
•C
30
20
10

RAINFALL

cm
60
50
40
30
20
10
0

244

Vegetation data from T.C. Whitmore, *A Vegetation Map of Malesia*, Reprinted from Journal of Biogeography Vol.11 (1984), pp461–471

KEY *(for both maps)*

——— international boundary
– – – state boundary
▲ peak or spot height

montane rainforest
lowland rainforest
grasslands, agriculture, misc. use
limestone vegetation
peat swampforest
freshwater swampforest
mangrove and tidal swamp

National Parks

1	Bako	5	Niah
2	Kinabalu	6	Taman Negara
3	Lambir Hills	7	Tengku Abdul
4	Mulu		Rahman

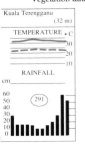

Kuala Terengganu (32 m)
TEMPERATURE °C
RAINFALL
cm
291

SINGAPORE (10 m)
TEMPERATURE °C
RAINFALL
cm
241

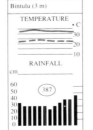

Bintulu (3 m)
TEMPERATURE °C
RAINFALL
cm
387

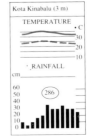

Kota Kinabalu (3 m)
TEMPERATURE °C
RAINFALL
cm
286

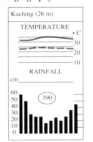

Kuching (26 m)
TEMPERATURE °C
RAINFALL
cm
390

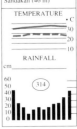

Sandakan (46 m)
TEMPERATURE °C
RAINFALL
cm
314

There is plenty of scope for enjoying the plant life, both wild and cultivated, on roadsides, plantations, vegetable and commercial gardens, *kampung*, ricefields and waste ground. It should be noted, however, that these more easily accessible places have vegetation greatly modified by man, and have a reduced number of native plant species and an increased number of aliens.

Access to undisturbed forest is usually difficult because most of it has been logged or cleared, or because of the dense growth which quickly develops at the forest edge. Streams and rivers and timber tracks may provide access to these areas.

Furthermore, there has been a serious degradation of the mountain flora in most of the places where it is accessible. I can only appeal to the good side of each of us to do nothing to worsen the situation, such as by trampling, picking or uprooting the plants. After all, photographs can be so much more satisfying than the dying remains of plants.

In the Peninsula

The extensive sandy shores of the east coast are easily reached as they are a popular holiday destination. A selection of such shore plants shown on pages 64–71 may be found here. However, the original beach forest is usually absent or damaged by fire and coconut plantations. Some vestiges of beach forest can be found on the rocky headlands, especially in Terengganu, and there is still some beach forest just south of the Desaru resort and Kuala Sedili Kecil at the end of Teluk Makhota (Jason's Bay).

Mangrove and freshwater swamp-forest are usually difficult to reach by land, and they are only easily accessible at high tide (where waters are tidal) and by boat, the smaller, the better. The mangrove is most extensive west of Taiping, Perak, while the tidal swampforest of Sedili Besar was studied by Corner. The shallow lakes of Tasek Bera and Tasek Cini in Pahang have interesting aquatic vegetation.

All the hill-stations are worth visiting for their plant life. Elfin forest can be seen on the ridge tops beside the roads up to the highest points in the Cameron and Genting highlands. Gunung Jerai (Kedah Peak), although only 1,217 metres high, has many species of attractive and unusual plants growing in its poor soil. Gunung Panti, a small flat-topped hill north of Kota Tinggi, in south Johor, has a remarkable number of endemic species in its heath forest. It is not easily accessible, but some of its endemics grow at the nearby Lombong waterfall, too.

The lower parts of limestone cliffs are easily accessible at Batu Caves, near Kuala Lumpur, around the Cave Temples on the main trunk road just south of Ipoh, in Kedah and Perlis and a few places in Kelantan and Pahang. Limestone vegetation can also be found on Pulau Langkawi, which is just south of the Thai-Malaysia border.

Taman Negara is the only National Park in the Peninsula (numbered 6 on the map on p.10). It has a large (4,300 square kilometres), undamaged area of dry lowland forest. There are frequent tours leaving Kuala Lumpur for Taman Negara. In addition, the Forest Department has established 39 Forest Recreation Areas in Kedah, Negeri Sembilan and Pahang. Each is centred on a natural feature such as a waterfall and has a cleared area with some of the trees labelled. There may be virgin forest near by.

Perlis and northwest Kedah have a monsoon flora like that of south Thailand, and considerably different from that of the rest of Malaysia. The best time to see this is around November for Pulau Langkawi and December for Perlis, at the start of the dry season.

The Arboretum of the Forest Research Institute at Kepong near Kuala Lumpur, the Waterfall Gardens in Georgetown, Pulau Pinang, and the Rimba Ilmu, Universiti Malaya, Petaling Jaya, are the principal gardens of botanical interest.

In Sarawak and Sabah

Downstream from Kuching in Sarawak there are still some extensive mangroves on the waterway to Bako National Park (numbered 1 on the map on p.11). Here are found *Sonneratia alba* mangroves accessible by catwalk and an interesting impoverished heath forest (*kerengas*) with small trees bearing large numbers of epiphytic ant plants. It also has the small-leaved conifer *Dacrydium pectinatum* and *Casuarina nobilis*. On the way up to the heath forest you can see the gigantic fan palm *Johannesteijsmannia altifrons* and the stemless *Eugeissona insignis*.

A long day's journey from Miri is the Mulu National Park (number 4) with its superlative limestone caves and mountains. Nearer at hand are the Lambir Hills National Park (number 2), with accessible lowland forest, and the Niah National Park (number 5), with its limestone hills and caves reached by a catwalk through swampy limestone forest.

The 75-square-kilometre Kinabalu National Park (number 3) is two hours by road from Kota Kinabalu, Sabah. It has lower montane forest with footpaths near the headquarters. The plant lover should plan to spend more than the three days it takes to climb the mountain, as the route to the summit is truly wonderful, passing through an area of great species diversity to the barren heights where only a few species of plant can survive.

Another park of interest near Kota Kinabalu is the Tengku Abdul Rahman National Park (number 7) on Gaya Island, with good beach forest. There is also a Forest Department Arboretum at Sepilok, near Sandakan, and the Orchid Research Centre near Tenom in the central part of the state.

The beautiful blossoms of Didymocarpus atrosanguinea *and the orchid* Tainia *sp. may be found in Taman Negara.*

ALONG THE COASTS

MARINE PLANTS

In shallow tropical seas where sufficient light penetrates there are microscopic drifting algae (phytoplankton), and larger algae (the seaweeds) which are attached to the bottom. On coral reefs, such as those of the islands off the east coasts of the Malay Peninsula and Sabah, the most important algae are the microscopic, single-celled Zooxanthellae which live within the tissues of most species of coral polyps. They are essential to the polyps' nutrition as they synthesize sugars. There are also small algae impregnated with calcium carbonate which play a part in building up the reef. A few larger algae, such as the Bunch-of-grapes Seaweed (p.73) also grow on the reef.

There are hundreds of species of seaweed in equatorial waters but they are smaller and form a sparser growth than those of the temperate regions. It is still not clear why this is so, but the generally lower concentration of nutrients in tropical waters and the hot sun, which can harm seaweeds exposed at low tide, may play a part. Only *Sargassum* species can grow several metres long and, buoyed up by small gas bladders, they can sometimes be seen forming a brown floating line beyond the low water tideline on the edges of coral flats.

Left: *The lower, brackish-water reaches of a small river in East Johor: by the riverside is the mangrove tree* Rhizophora apiculata, *with its very long stilt-roots. In the background, lowland forest can be seen, with the blue-grey crown of a* Seraya.

Right: *The brown seaweed (*Padina sp.*) and the green seaweed (*Halimeda sp.*) can be seen at low tide on sandy coral flats.*

15

By contrast, Malaysian coasts are rich in the so-called 'sea grasses' (p.73). There are five species of these flowering plants, all belonging to the Hydrocharitaceae, which usually take root in the mud or sand of coral flats.

MANGROVES

On waterlogged, muddy shores and estuaries, wherever there is sufficient protection from waves, there grows a unique saltwater forest — the mangrove. It is virtually confined to the tropics, and Malaysia and its neighbours have the largest number of mangrove species in the world.

Mangrove only occupies the upper half of the intertidal zone, and the up-

At high tide the mangrove provides food and shelter for marine life. The high prop-roots are characteristic of Rhizophora apiculata.

per part of this may be bare where it is too sandy and well-drained. Wherever the shore is muddy and the terrain flat, mangrove merges gradually into freshwater swampforest.

In the whole tropical world, there are only about 60 species of trees and a few shrubs, climbers and herbs which can be considered mangrove plants in the strict sense, that is able to survive in undiluted seawater and unable to grow successfully in freshwater. About one half of these grow in Malaysia. This small number shows that mangrove, with its salty water and waterlogged, oxygen-poor soils, is a hostile environment for higher plants.

The plants of the mangrove have several pecularities which probably promote survival. Though the mangrove is permanently wet, there is also abundant salt which is absorbed along with water by the roots. However, when the water is evaporated from the leaves, the salt is left behind. The more seawater is absorbed, the more salt accumulates in the plant, and the more water is needed by the plant. In this sense the environment is physiologically dry, and this is probably why mangrove plants, like desert plants and those of temperate salt marshes, tend to have thick fleshy leaves, which may reduce water loss.

Besides having fleshy leaves, most trees in the mangrove are able to absorb water with a lower concentration of salt than that in which the roots stand. Some of the salt is held back, by the metabolic activities of the roots and not by a simple filtration process. Besides this, some plants such as *Jeruju* (p.72) and the *Api-api* trees (*Avicennia* spp.) have special glands on the leaves which excrete a salt solution more concentrated than that in the sap. After a long period of dry weather, it may be possible to see the salt on the leaves as whitish patches.

The main root system of mangrove trees is partly in the air and contains spongy tissues which let oxygen pass through to the parts of the roots buried in the airless mud. Air enters the aerial roots through numerous corky pores, or lenticels, when these dry out at low tide. On some coasts the surface level of the mud is constantly rising, and the aerial root system provides a base from which new small feeding roots can grow out into the well-aerated surface mud, where alone they can survive. There are several forms of aerial roots. *Rhizophora* trees have branching stilt-roots (pp.16, 74). *Sonneratia* (pp.78–9) and *Avicennia* have cylindrical peg-roots projecting into the air, while *Bruguiera* has knee-roots which grow upwards above ground and then turn abruptly downwards. *Heritiera littoralis* (*Dungun* in Malay) has roots which are greatly flattened from side to side projecting well above the mud, like gigantic tapes.

Some mangrove tree species flower when very small, and have unusual means of dispersal. Nearly all flowering plant species produce seeds, which are a specialized resting form of the plant with protective coatings enclosing a dried and concentrated food reserve and an embryonic root and shoot. In most mangrove tree species, such as those belonging to the Rhizophoraceae, the embryo continues to develop in the fruit and only stops after producing a well-developed green plantlet,* which is the resting and dispersal phase of the plant. When it finally falls, it may stick in the mud like a javelin and

---

* One of the few mangrove herbs, *Keladi Laut* (p.72) also produces well-developed plantlets.

This brackish-water tidal creek has the beautiful and useful Nipa palm growing in it. The leaves of this plant are used for atap roofing, while the sweet, gelatinous fruit is an important ingredient in ice kacang.

develop rapidly; or it may float, maybe for months, before lodging and developing on a distant shore. This is probably why mangrove species are widely distributed on the tropical shores of the world. It seems that a typical resting seed is disadvantageous to a plant that is never likely to experience dry conditions.

Mangroves are productive and useful forests. The timber of *Rhizophora* especially is in great demand for scaffold poles, firewood, charcoal and for piling, as it has a rather undeserved reputation for not rotting underwater. Cutch was produced from the bark; this was used for tanning leather, sails and nets, which it stained rust-red.

Rhizophora forests are most extensive on the Perak coast, especially southwest of Taiping, where they were the first Malaysian forests to be managed by silvicultural methods, with clear-felling every 30 years. Regeneration is usually excellent after felling, providing the ground is cleared of dead brushwood, which prevents seedlings from floating in. Otherwise, the giant fern *Piai Raya* (p.75) can establish itself and prevent tree regeneration by the deep shade it casts.

As mangrove is an important feeding ground for young fish and prawns, which swim in at high tide, its destruction lowers the productivity of nearby waters. Considerable areas near the larger coastal towns have been destroyed by land-fill for building, while sea walls and tidal drains have been constructed in the countryside to convert large areas of mangrove into coconut plantations and prawn ponds.

Wherever the mangrove zone is wide enough, the heavy runoff at high tide carves deep channels through the mud, but where a river runs to the sea, muddy banks are lined by mangroves. As the salinity diminishes upstream, the mangrove species disappear gradually except for the *Beremban* tree (pp.78–9), the *Nipa* palm (p.77) and the *Piai Raya* fern (p.74–75), which persist as far as there is salt in the water.

ROCKY AND SANDY SHORES

Although the roots of beach plants growing on the shore may be very close to the sea at high tide, salinity is probably much lower than in mangrove. This is because of the underground reservoir of fresh water derived from the heavy rainfall, which slowly flows from the land towards the sea.

Where the shore is rocky or sandy, the upper part of the foreshore is bare of vegetation, though in very protected places, as at Santubong near Kuching, grass-like sedges may grow on sand. Where beaches are rising by the deposition of sand, pioneer herbs just above the high tidemark are the Sea Morning Glory (p.70) and several sedges and grasses, including Spinifex Grass (*Spinifex littorale*; *Lari-lari*), which has spherical female fruit-heads that become detached and blow along the beach. Other beach herbs are the alien Periwinkle (p.71) and three species of bean — two *Canavalia* species (p.70) and the yellow-flowered *Vigna marina*. Bare sand on growing beaches is often colonized by *Casuarina equisetifolia* trees, which in suitable places can form an unbroken narrow ribbon of forest along the beach, as can be seen along the east coast of Peninsular Malaysia and the west coast of Sabah.

Other shore trees grow on undisturbed sandy or rocky shores. However, trees on most accessible sandy shores have been destroyed by fire and replaced by coarse grassland. Coconuts are often planted behind sandy beaches and can survive even when the ground between the root masses is washed away by the sea.

Where the coast is rocky, trees and shrubs predominate. Only a few species are able to establish themselves on the seaward strip so they are easily identified, especially as they usually fruit and flower freely, and have branches and trunks that may spread out low over the foreshore. Some of these are illustrated on pages 64–9, but there are others. These include the *Jambu Laut* (*Eugenia grandis*), which is often used for roadside planting; the mango-like *Buchanania arborescens* with its creamy flowers and small black inedible fruit and the Sea Fig (*Ficus superba*), both are beautiful trees which should be planted by the roadside. Then there is the *Buah Keras Laut* (*Hernandia nymphaeifolia*), which has a black nut set in a waxy-white fleshy inflated cup with an opening in the top, and *Pongamia pinnata*, with pinkish pea-flowers. Coastal treelets include the *Mentigi* (*Pemphis acidula*) and the *Petai Laut* (*Desmodium umbellatum*).

Strand trees have a wider natural distribution through the tropics than tropical forest trees. This is probably because most have floating fruits whose seeds remain viable for months and will germinate when washed ashore. The notable exception is the Casuarina with its small wind-borne seeds.

Behind the sandy beaches of Malaysia there is often a series of low sandy ridges marking the position of earlier shorelines. These ridges (or *permatang*) were once covered by heath forest, but this is often degraded by fire to scrub, savanna or grassland which may be maintained by fire or grazing and is extremely deficient in mineral nutrients. The intervening strips of lowland may be freshwater swamps and can support a richer plant life.

An exposed coast in Peninsular Malaysia: a few straggly Casuarinas can just be seen near the tide-line. This forest has been greatly reduced by wind, and possibly by fire — the coastal forest is usually much more luxuriant.

FRESHWATER WET PLACES

FRESHWATER SWAMPFOREST

Above the level of saltwater penetration, on tidal floodplains and wherever the ground is flat enough, there stands (or stood) freshwater swampforest. During the rainy season the ground may be flooded to a depth of several metres, and the trees must be able to survive this. On the other hand, during dry weather this may dry out leaving a network of small shallow channels with an almost imperceptible rate of flow, and the undergrowth may become so dry that it can burn. My impression is that swampforests are more likely to burn than dry land tropical rainforests. The extensive swampy grasslands north of Air Hitam, Johor, are probably the end result of repeated swampforest fires.

Corner, in 1978, published a memorable account of the swampforest of Sungei Sedili Kecil in Johor ("The Freshwater Swampforest of South Johor and Singapore", *Gardens Bulletin*, Singa-

Tidal freshwater swampforest at high tide, Sedili Besar River, Johor. The pole-like stems of Rasau (Pandanus helicopus) *are crowned with long leaves which bend sharply downwards. Under them are clumps of the low shrub* Putat Air (Barringtonia conoidea). *Behind is the useful, thorny* Nibung *palm* (Oncosperma tigillarium).

pore, v.30, suppl.1). It is imbued with the feeling of excitement and wonder at such an exuberant celebration of nature which, he wrote, was not equalled in variety and grandeur even by the Amazonian forest. He expresses his sadness and outrage at its passing:

"Jason's Bay, once so secluded and beautiful with high forest terminating in the fringe of *Casuarina* overhanging the waves, has been transformed by logging and reckless deforestation into a hot, fractured and unattractive landscape."

Most of this swampforest has been cleared, though in many places a thin fringe of surviving trees remains along the riverbanks. Corner found that most of the swampforest trees were different species from those growing on dry ground. Aerial roots of various forms resembling those in mangroves occurred in about 200 tree species. Thus there are stilt-roots, knee-roots and wedge-shaped roots.

Many of the swampforests with good soils have been cleared to form the great rice-growing areas of the states of Kedah, Pulau Pinang, Selangor, Melaka, Kelantan and Terengganu, as well as parts of the west coast of Sabah. In other places along the plains of the west coast of Peninsular Malaysia, deep drains have been dug to lower the water-table sufficiently for the cultivation of tree crops and Pine-apples.

Starting from the sea and going up a river like the Sedili Besar, the traveller passes successive types of tidal river-side vegetation in each of which one or a few species predominate. First there is mangrove, and then comes the *Nipa* palm (p.17) and *Beremban* (pp.78-9), which do not require salt and usually live where the water is only slightly brackish. Further upstream *Putat Air* (*Barringtonia conoidea*; p.20) begins to appear. This extraordinary shrub with its clump of upright conical trunks sticking up from the riverside mudbank looks, when young, as if it had been designed as a flexible fend-off for boats. This is not such a fanciful resemblance, as it may help the tree to withstand the impact of floating tree trunks which crash past during floods. There are also dense forests of the pole-like *Rassau* (*Pandanus helicopus*; p.20)

with the infamous but beautiful *Rengas Air* (*Gluta velutina*), which belongs to the same family as the Mango and Poison Ivy and whose black resin can devastate the skin of people who have become sensitized to it.

One particular kind of swampfor-est which is found in Terengganu and Melaka is dominated by the Paper Bark Tree (*Gelam*; *Melaleuca leucaden-dra*). It may be the result of repeated burning; this tree survives burning be-cause of its thick soft bark, and its ability to produce shoots from the low-er parts of the trunk.

Peat swampforest is a special type which develops under conditions of acidity and oxygen lack which inhibit bacterial decomposition of vegetable matter and leads to the accumulation of peat. In Sarawak, where it occupies about ten per cent of the land area, the peat forms domes up to ten metres high. The poorest tree growth is in the centre of the dome, which is entirely watered by rain, and so is very defi-cient in mineral salts. The soil becomes progressively richer towards the peri-phery of the dome because of minerals leached from the centre, thus produc-ing high forest. Such peat swamps are valuable timber resources which tend to regenerate with the original species, but they are useless for agriculture. In some Sarawak forests of this type, *Shorea albida* is the dominant tree.

Left: *Rooted in the mud is* Cryptocoryne griffithii, *while the roots of a woody plant trail in the clear waters of a sluggish stream.*

Right (top): *Typical aquatic vegetation in a roadside canal in Kedah: floating plants of the Water Hyacinth (p.80), together with Turtle Grass (p.83), Waterlilies* (Nymphaea stellata) *and Yellow Bur-head (p.80) can be seen. The trailing stems with the whitish-mauve, trumpet-shaped flowers and spear-point-shaped leaves are those of the edible Kangkung* (Ipomoea aquatica).

Right (bottom): *The water's edge of Dingkil Swampforest in Selangor.*

HERBS OF WET PLACES

Many of the wet places in Malaysia are the results of human activity, such as ricefields, drainage canals, borrow pits on the sides of roads and railways, fishponds, reservoirs and mining pools. Natural habitats include the occasional ox-bow lake, depressions between beach ridges and small forest streams, whose bottoms are often covered with the beautiful, mottled leaves of *Cryptocoryne* species (pp.18, 82). Most of the lower reaches of Malaysia's rivers are heavily polluted, but even the few remaining clear-water rivers are often devoid of higher water plants.

The submerged parts of water plants are delicate and cannot withstand drying. Some water plants are free floaters and are not rooted in the mud. These include Water Hyacinth (p.80) and Water Lettuce (*Kiambang*; *Pistia stratiotes*). Both are introduced species and Chinese farmers grow them as pig food. There are also two small floating ferns: a species of *Azolla*, which contains the blue-green alga *Anabaena azollae* that converts atmospheric nitrogen into plant nutrients and so is worth encouraging, and Water Spangle (*Salvinia cucullata*), a Tropical American native which is larger and has silvery-haired, concave oval fronds.

Native submerged floaters include the carnivorous Golden Bladderwort (p.83), its feathery leaves bearing tiny bladders which are suction traps for minute aquatic animals. Native surface floaters are Duckweeds (*Lemna* spp.) whose three-millimetre, plate-like stems can exploit the smallest patches of open water. Even tinier than Duckweed is the seldom-seen *Wolffia arrhiza*; at 1.5 millimetres diameter, it is the world's smallest flowering plant.

Water plants rooted on the bottom include Waterlilies (*Nymphaea* spp.) with cleft, circular floating leaf-blades on stems as long as the water is deep, and the related Sacred Lotus (p.81).

There are also ferns that grow in standing water: *Paku Roman* (*Ceratopteris thalictroides*) with narrow frondlets, and two species of *Marsilea*. These are common ricefield weeds.

Some plants can live as floaters on open water and rooted in the earth of moist ground, such as the edible *Kangkung* (or Water Convolvulus; p.23) and *Ludwigia adscendens* (p.82).

WATERFALLS

The force of falling water is too great for higher plants to survive, so rocks are bare up to the flood level. However, spray keeps the surroundings wet and the air permanently saturated with vapour. Thus rocks near the bottom of the waterfall are heavily colonized by liverworts, mosses, selaginellas and ferns, especially the filmy ferns, which require moisture and shade. Flowering plants common in such sites include various species of *Impatiens* (p.99) with their flattened flowers and carpets of *Elatostema*, while *Begonias* are common on rocks beyond the spray zone.

RHEOPHYTES

Some plants are able to withstand weeks of submergence and the pull of fast-flowing water during floods. They grow on the banks or stony beaches of swift-flowing rivers above the usual water level. They have been called rheophytes. Most are firmly anchored shrubs, with branches often bent by the force of the water and bearing long and narrow, or small, tough, shiny leaves or leaflets. They include species of fig, an Ixora (p.84), *Aglaia ysermannii*, *Dysoxylum angustifolium* (p.85), *Calophyllum rupicolum*, and *Phyllanthus watsonii*, known only from Endau–Rompin. *Saraca* species form dense stands along fast-flowing lowland torrents. These often start life as a rheophyte

and later grow up to be a medium-sized tree.

The fruits of some rheophytes are eaten and their seeds dispersed by fish, for example *Dysoxylum angustifolium* (p.85). Some plants familiar from other sites may grow in the boulder-strewn areas, such as Straits Rhododendron (*Melastoma malabathricum*; p.46), the alien Golden Candlesticks (p.117) and the Bamboo Orchid (p.124).

It would be worthwhile experimenting with the cultivation of rheophytes. Many are beautiful and can survive under extreme conditions, so they might even be able to tolerate the conditions of city life.

Far left: *Carson's Falls, Kinabalu National Park. The small pink flower is that of Borneo Balsam* (Impatiens platyphylla), *while the large leaves belong to a* Piptospatha *species.*

Below: *The beautiful rheophyte* Aglaia ysermannii *often grows on riverbanks.*

TROPICAL LOWLAND EVERGREEN RAINFOREST

Only three decades ago, most of Malaysia was covered with a mantle of the kind of vegetation often called tropical rainforest. In the Peninsula nearly all lowland forest has been logged, and the same will soon be true of Sabah and Sarawak. Much of it has now been replaced by monocultures of commercially valuable tree crops.

Rainforest is poorly understood as a system because of its complexity. But this kind of vegetation, which is also called primary or virgin forest — *hutan rimba* or *hutan belantara* — has major characteristics that distinguish it from secondary forest — *belukar*.

SPECIES DIVERSITY

Nowhere in the world is there such diversity of trees as in tropical rainforest, and this may be true of the smaller life-forms too, such as small animals and lower plants. More tree species may grow in a few hectares of apparently uniform ground than in all the forests and woodlands of Europe with its vast area and wide range of climatic conditions! It is usual to find about 200 species of tree in an area of one to two hectares, while those of a similar area of temperate forest may be counted on the fingers of one hand.

It is not clear why there are so many species co-existing with one another while competing for limited resources such as light, space and nutrients, and there are probably many reasons. Malaysia has received contributions of plants from both Laurasia and Gondwanaland, the great north and south landmasses of ancient times. The only Malaysian forests with few tree species — the mangrove and strand forest — are unfavourable environments, suggesting that favourable conditions have played a part. Their apparent persistence for perhaps 100 million years could have provided time for the evolution of many species without mass extinctions from catastrophes like ice ages. Also, predatory insects with highly specific food preferences are less likely to cause extinctions when host trees of the same species are widely separated, as is often the case.*

The rainforest appears uniform when seen from a distance. However,

---

The future of the forest: a seedling of a Shorea, *probably the most important genus of timber trees in Malaysia. The prospects of artificial reforestation with such trees are poor because seeds are produced every few years and only survive for a few days.*

---

* An extreme example of the sparseness of individuals of a tree species is provided by *Glenniea philippinensis*, known from only one individual each in Sabah and Luzon, Philippines, and a few in the Peninsula (Melaka and Pulau Pinang)!

it is complex in structure and contains large numbers of plant and animal species at different stages of development. The network of relationships between the species, each of which may have its own optimal environmental conditions, is so complex it still defies analysis. This great range of micro-habitats may be a cause for further diversity of species.

There are, however, a few situations where one species may predominate in the forest. Thus the distinctive, blue-grey-leaved *Seraya* (*Shorea curtisii*; p.14), with the *Bertam* palm (*Eugeissona tristis*), underneath, dominates many dry ridges. The Borneo Camphor Tree , or *Kapur* (*Dryobalanops aromatica*), Borneo Ironwood (*Eusidero-*

The banks of this clear-water lowland river in Peninsular Malaysia, in Taman Negara, are lined with Neram (Dipterocarpus oblongifolius), *which characteristically lean out over the river, and various rheophytic shrubs.*

xylon zwageri) and the *Shorea albida* of Borneo peat swamps are also strongly dominant in some places.

TREES

Trees constitute most of the species of flowering plants as well as the biomass, and may predominate even at ground level in the form of saplings. The tallest tree is the *Tualang* (*Koompassia excelsa*), which regularly grows to a height of 60 metres and has a trunk 1.5 metres in diameter. Most of the other tall trees are members of the Dipterocarp family and often exceed 45 metres in height.

Most of the tallest trees which have survived the enormous odds against reaching maturity in the forest end up with a similar shape when their crowns reach the canopy: the trunk is straight and tapers only slightly, branches only appear about two-thirds of the way up, and the crown is mushroom-shaped. Many species have buttresses at the base of the trunk, apparently produced in response to tension stresses in the roots. Thus they are more marked on the uphill side of slopes, and the *Neram*, which leans over the rivers in Taman Negara National Park, and in Sarawak, has a single buttress on its uphill side. Buttresses may provide some protection against being blown down.

Root systems are usually shallow, and it is common for trees to be uprooted. Most forest tree species have moderate-sized evergreen leaves of 10–20 centimetres long. They are oval, shiny, thick and leathery, and are resistant to insect attack except when very young. Leaves are produced continuously in only a few species; most produce leaves in 'flushes' occurring once or twice a year — this discourages predators which feed on young leaves. These flushes may involve only a part of the tree, as in some of the relatives of the Mango. At any time of the year, some trees will be producing new leaves, and new-leaf production in Selangor and Negeri Sembilan has been found to reach a peak two or three months after the main rainy season.

While most of the forest trees are evergreen with leaves which last for more than a year and are shed continuously, a few trees such as the wild *Kapok* (*Bombax valetonii*), the orange-flowered *Mata Lembu* (*Firmiana malayana*) and the Yellow Flame (*Peltophorum pterocarpum*; p.61) are deciduous and may shed their leaves all at once before new leaves emerge.

Other pecularities have been observed in some forest species. These include the elongated tips of many hanging leaves and leaflets. These "drip tips" (p.26) have been shown to speed up the drying of leaf-blades, and probably diminish the leaching of nutrients, but this seems to have little effect in discouraging the growth of micro-epiphytes. Another oddity is for young leaves of some species to be brightly coloured — red, purple or mauve — and the reasons for this are obscure. Also some trees bear flowers and fruit on main branches or even the trunk. In the case of the Cempedak and Durian, their small branches could not support the heavy fruit. It used to be fashionable to ascribe the existence of these pecularities to various advantages they were supposed to confer, but the present attitude is one of scepticism.

HERBS

Climatic conditions on the forest floor are extremely constant. Since about only one to two per cent of the light falling on the canopy reaches the forest floor, and this is mainly of wavelengths useless for photosynthesis, conditions are not conducive to rapid growth of herbs, though these may be present in considerable quantity, and are patchily distributed.

Ground herbs include a large proportion of ferns. All are shade tolerant, but some, like the filmy ferns, are shade demanding. The Arum, African Violet (p.90) and Ginger (pp.92–3) families are each represented by many species. By contrast only a few broad-leaved and shade-tolerant grass species occur. There are, however, about 50 species of Bamboo, giant woody members of the Grass family, mainly growing in disturbed places. Unlike those of temperate woodlands, humid tropical forest herbs have no resting phase (with the exception of *Amorphophallus*; p.120), and even stout rhizomes may have little food reserve.

CLIMBERS

Large woody climbers, or lianas, such as Rattans (p.31) start life on the forest floor, often with a rosette of leaves. They may remain fairly low for a long time until a gap which lets in sufficient light develops. They then undergo a phase of rapid upward growth without branching, often with small, widely spaced leaves. They have some means of fixation to the trees on which they climb, such as by twining round the trunk, or by tendrils or hooks. On climbing out of the shadows, lianas may give up their climbing habit and produce shorter or hanging branches with larger leaves and flowering shoots. This climbing habit allows a plant with only a slender stem to reach the light.

Large woody climbers do no major damage to trees in the high forest, though they may reach the canopy. However, they may pull down neighbouring trees when a climber-covered large tree falls or is cut down. Logging, by letting in light, often encourages a dense growth of climbers, which can seriously interfere with the forest's regeneration by shading out saplings.

EPIPHYTES

Epiphytes are herbs or shrubs which

are attached by their roots to the trunks or branches of trees. This mode of life enables a small epiphyte in the forest to obtain access to bright light, but at a cost of being exposed to hot, dry conditions and of being cut off from that great reservoir of water and nutrients — the soil. Epiphytes can live away from trees and they are sometimes found on bare rocks, especially in the mountains.

They do not extract nutrients from the live tissues of the tree on which they perch, so do little or no harm. The exceptions are the members of the Mistletoe family (p.132) and a few other hemi-parasitic shrubs whose specialized roots penetrate the wood of their host tree. The host provides the mistletoes with their water and mineral nutrients and is weakened by this, as can often be seen from the poor growth of leaves on parasitized tree limbs. However, hemi-parasites have green leaves which produce sugars.

Many epiphytes have fleshy leaves. Orchids often have thickened stem bases, or pseudo-bulbs; some ferns have thick stems and a few other epiphytes have tubers. All these store water, which helps the plant to withstand dry conditions. Many epiphytic species share with desert species a special kind of metabolism, which allows carbon dioxide to be absorbed at night, when water loss is minimal, and stored until the next day when it is used for photosynthesis.

Nearly all species of epiphyte are dispersed by wind. This includes the ferns and other lower plants, which have microscopic spores, and the orchids and Lipstick Plants (p.96) with minute seeds. *Hoya* (p.134) and *Dischidia* have silk-tasselled seeds which, in *Dischidia nummularia* at least, are sticky. *Hydnophytum*, *Myrmecodia* (p.136) and the mistletoes, on the other hand, have berries whose seeds are distributed by birds, but ants have also been seen carrying them.

The larger epiphytes tend to establish themselves on surfaces already colonized by small lower plants like algae and mosses. There is little humus where epiphytes take root, and some large epiphytic ferns like the Bird's Nest Fern (*Sarang Langsuir; Asplenium nidus*), Stag's Horn Fern (*Semun Bidadari; Platycerium coronarium*) and the Oak Leaf Fern (*Drynaria quercifolia*) trap falling vegetable matter, by means of special stiff nest-leaves in the case of the latter two. (The humus nest of the Stag's Horn Fern sometimes reaches massive proportions.)

Many epiphytes are associated with ants, which bring up soil from below. Some epiphytes have specialized structures where ants live and multiply, and so are called ant plants. Such plants include *Myrmecodia* (p.136) and *Hydnophytum formicarium* — Baboon's Head — with their swollen, honeycombed, water-storing stems, and *Dischidia major* with its hollow, pitcherlike leaves. Several other *Dischidia* species (p.136) lave cupped leaves pressed close to the tree, under which ants take refuge. Some *Hoya* species have clusters of leaves wit h their edges pressed together; ants live in the centre of these leaf clusters.

STRANGLING FIGS

These remarkable trees start life as epiphytic shrubs germinating on trees, usually in a fork between branches or

Things seen in the forest. Top: *The tough leathery leaves of some shrubs may become covered with micro-epiphytes, lichens, algae and even mosses over the years.* Bottom left: *The spiny stem of a climbing Rattan palm* (Daemonorops didymophylla) *bears a load of scaly fruit. These are covered with a red resin, used as a dye and in traditional medicine.* Bottom right: *Many kinds of fungi grow on dead tree trunks. The white one is a species of Bracket Fungus, the orange one is* Gymnopilus dilepis.

on masonry. They put down aerial roots which may encircle the host tree's trunk and may form, by self-grafting, a stout basket-like network of roots; other hanging roots may reach the ground and become thickened tree trunks. Stranglers often survive their host tree, but the old idea that the host was strangled is probably wrong as the basketwork of roots does not cut grooves into the trunk (as is the case with lianas on quite healthy trees). In the later stage of life, these fig trees may damage the host tree by shading or by competing with it for root space.

LAYERS AND GAPS IN THE FOREST

Tropical lowland evergreen rain-

A strangling fig growing on a large tree which it will eventually replace.

forest can be described by grouping together trees and other plants of different height ranges into a series of layers, from treetop to ground level.

The top layer consists of the crowns of the tallest trees, the emergents. Only certain species, mostly the commercially valuable Dipterocarps, are able to reach this level, which has numerous gaps. The second layer is the main canopy, which is more complete except under the emergents and in newly formed gaps. This is the layer reached by big lianas. The third layer consists of spindly trees with narrow trunks; the fourth has the shrubs, treelets, saplings and large herbs, while the fifth includes tree seedlings and small herbs.

The different layers of the forest have different micro-climates. Above the forest canopy, conditions resemble those in the open places, with a daily temperature range of about 10°C and a relative humidity varying from nearly 100 per cent to about 60 per cent. At the forest floor the temperature is about 3°C lower and the daily range may be as little as 3°C. In wet weather the relative humidity may stay above 90 per cent for days on end.

The forest layers are seldom complete and lack precise boundaries. It is also obvious that all trees (except for epiphytes and stranglers) in higher levels have grown up from the ground. A more useful approach is to think of the forest as something that is constantly changing: a giant tree is the survivor of a large number of seedlings that persisted as spindly trees in the third layer until the death of a nearby tall tree provided the light that was needed to grow more rapidly to break through to the canopy.

If a big tree is uprooted or the trunk broken, a larger gap is suddenly produced. This may let in so much sunlight that some of the established seedlings may be killed off by the heat. Any bare patch of ground will then become populated by light-demanding, short-lived pioneer tree species, such as *Macaranga* (pp.35,113) and other related trees, and *Trema*. These in turn are replaced by 'climax' species, which develop in the shade of the pioneers.

The reproductive strategies of the most valuable timber trees discourage their replacement after major human disturbance. Unlike pioneer species, nearly all species of Dipterocarp trees flower infrequently, usually after an exceptionally dry period. This results in gregarious fruiting of many species every few years. The fruit, although winged like a shuttlecock (pp.87,89), are mostly heavy and, in the comparatively windless equatorial forests, usually fall close to the parent tree. Furthermore, the seeds die quickly if they do not germinate: *Seraya* seeds begin to lose viability within one week. This may not matter under natural conditions, but it means that seeds are unlikely to be available when they are needed for the natural regeneration in gaps after logging. Replanting from seed is not a practical proposition except in special cases, and vegetative propagation is still an experimental procedure and not widespread.

HEATH FOREST

This special type of rainforest develops on podsols — leached, silicious white-sand soils overlying a hard, black humus and iron oxide pan. These forests are common only in Sarawak, where they are called *kerangas,* an Iban word for terrain where dryland rice cannot be grown. It usually is a dense forest of pole-like trees of a limited number of species. These have small leathery leaves which are light-coloured, or sometimes reddish. Where the soils are poorest, the most striking feature is the prevalence of epiphytic ant plants, as in the Bako National Park near Kuching. The occurrence of carnivorous plants like *Nepenthes* (pp.94,130) probably indicates nitrogen deficiency in the soil.

Trees with greatly reduced leaves like the conifer *Dacrydium elatum,* *Casuarina nobilis* and *Baeckia fruticosa* are common, suggesting periods of water shortage, though mosses, typical of damp places, may also be common. On burning, heath forest may become secondary savanna — grassland with occasional trees. This kind of vegetation is extensive along the east coast of Peninsular Malaysia, where only two small areas of heath forest survive in Pahang. There are interesting heath forests on Gunung Jerai (Kedah Peak) , on the flat top of Gunung Panti, Johor, near Kota Tinggi, and in the Endau–Rompin area.

FOREST PRODUCTIVITY

The production of useful wood in the tree trunks in rainforests has been estimated to be 4–12 tonnes per hectare per year, similar to that of temperate forests. However, total productivity is much higher as it includes growth of all the other parts of the tree and losses by shedding of leaves and other parts, and by respiration. Of course if we consider a large area of forest in equilibrium, the biomass increment is zero because net growth is balanced by the death and decomposition of large trees.

A single tree starts to increase in mass slowly, this speeds up until maturity and ultimately decreases in senescence as large branches die. Growth in height is very different, being rapid from the beginning and decreasing to a negligible value as soon as the adult shape is acquired.

It is difficult to determine the age of tropical trees as they lack annual growth rings. Growth rate studies on large Malaysian trees have yielded estimated ages of 60–500 years. The oldest known age for a Malaysian forest tree was an overmature *Seraya* about 800 years old by radiocarbon dating. Pioneer species are mostly short-lived, surviving for about 15–30 years, but some live longer, such as the *Kelempayan* (*Anthocephalus chinensis*; p.44), which has silvicultural potential, and *Pulai* (*Alstonia* spp.), whose lightweight timber can be used as a substitute for balsa wood.

The total biomass of the rainforest is very high, up to 500 tonnes per hectare. This has been thought to indicate an inexhaustible supply of nutrients for agriculture. In fact the soil is usually rather poor. The topsoil is only millimetres thick and the underlying subsoil of kaolinitic clay is heavily leached by the high rainfall, particularly in the acid conditions which prevail. The subsoil may be 10–15 metres thick, so the liberation of nutrients by the chemical weathering of bedrock takes place out of reach of the generally shallow root systems. The poverty of Malaysian soils is shown by the rapid fall-off of yield when herbaceous crops are grown continuously without fertilizers, and their slow recovery under fallow conditions.

Until recently it was thought that the mineral nutrients needed for tree growth were mainly in the living and dead vegetation. The importance of nutrients liberated by decomposing plant matter is suggested by the fact that the small feeding roots of trees are in the surface layers of the soil. They often grow up through the soil into the decomposing lower layers of the leaf litter and may form dense masses in peaty soil. New information now available shows great variations in the partition of nutrients between vegetation and soil in different places and for different nutrients. Certain nutrients are in fact located mainly in the soil and not in the vegetation; but soil phosphorus is mostly unavailable.

THREATS TO THE FOREST

Under natural conditions the lowland rainforests in Southeast Asia are remarkably stable in the face of natural events such as lightning strike, fire and windstorms, and floods in the case of swampforest.

In contrast, it is peculiarly vulnerable to modern-style logging. Once a large area has been cleared, whether for logging or for cultivation, there is little chance of its reverting to anything like its original state because of human population pressure. Even if it were then left undisturbed, the forest would need more than a lifetime to recover.

Logging

Since pre-war times the forest has been owned by the states; concessions to extract timber from specified areas were granted for a limited period. A few selected trees were hauled out by teams of buffaloes or men, little damage was done and fairly complete regeneration was usual. In the last 30 years, however, the rate of timber extraction has greatly increased, and forest departments in most Southeast Asian countries have lost much of their control of logging operations. The loggers, who are concerned with quick and maximum profit for minimum effort, often seem to have a free hand and the future of the forest is not their concern as they must give it up when the concession expires.

Much of the damage caused by logging is unnecessary. The Sarawak Forest Department has shown that by felling trees in the direction which causes least damage and by well-planned skidding of logs, damage to the remaining trees was halved, and the op-

Recent clear-felling allows an unobstructed view into the logged forest in the background where a giant Meranti (Shorea *sp.) can be seen, with its characteristic red-brown fissured bark. In the foreground, a dense mat of* Resam *ferns has shaded out all but a* Macaranga gigantea *(on the left, with the large, three-lobed leaves) and a* Rattan palm *(on the right).*

eration was quicker and cheaper! Present-day operators use huge heavy equipment which compresses the soil. This makes it nearly impervious to water and air, and very unfavourable for tree growth. Huge logs are hauled out by skidders which dig deep furrows that destroy the topsoil with its roots and seeds, and interfere with the drainage. On exposed steep slopes a layer of soil several centimetres thick may be lost by erosion in a few months, while earth from road building is tipped down hillsides.

When a large tree is felled, it damages many other trees as it falls. It was shown in Peninsular Malaysia that extraction of trees covering ten per cent of the area can destroy trees over a

Devastation created by careless logging operators. Many smaller trees have been destroyed by the felled trees and will not survive.

further 55 per cent of the area. So much light is thus let in that regeneration is by light-demanding, short-lived pioneer trees of no commercial value.

Fire

Virgin rainforest, unlike *belukar* will not burn, although a narrow strip is destroyed when a clearing is burned by shifting cultivators or when labourers clear a roadside edge by fire. However, there have been devastating forest fires in Sabah and over the border in Kalimantan after exceptionally dry weather in 1982–3. Shifting cultivators have been made the scapegoats, as have hunters who burn the forest to attract animals to the tender shoots which sprout after fire.

This does not explain why vast areas, amounting to 20 per cent of the area of Sabah in some opinions, have burned: something that has never

happened before, except in limited areas like the Sook and Keningau plains in Sabah. The underlying cause of the disaster is the change in the forest brought about largely by modern logging. Gaps between fallen trees and timber tracks allow the sun to dry the vegetation and they provide wind channels along which fire can spread. The edges of these tracks are well-supplied with flammable debris like the trimmed-off branches of trees.

One of the worst effects of fire is that, with the replacement of high forest by *belukar*, the forest again becomes potentially flammable in a few years' time, and remains so for many years. Furthermore, clearing forests liberates carbon dioxide when wood and other organic matter is burned or decomposes. This, and the burning of fossil fuels, is raising the carbon dioxide concentration of the atmosphere, which in turn threatens to warm up the world by the so-called "greenhouse effect", with possibly disastrous consequences to humankind.

The destruction of forests is not an inevitable consequence of logging, but rather the effect of careless over-exploitation with huge modern machines. There is no doubt that damage could be reduced to a more reasonable level by using less destructive extraction methods. For the future perhaps, new methods of extraction, such as those involving balloons or helicopters, will become economical and safe for large-scale use.

However, the need for immediate revenue by state governments which own the forests, and the desire for immediate profits by timber concession holders are powerful economic incentives. With such immediate pressures, dire predictions are unlikely to be heeded, so I cannot be optimistic. I cannot help thinking of Borneo as a kind of Garden of Eden, its harmony shattered by the short-term benefits from cutting down the tree of wealth.

What will happen when the trees and the wealth they bring are gone?

THREATS TO PLANT SPECIES

Knowledge of the numbers and distribution of plant species in Malaysia is so limited that it is difficult to say what extinctions have occurred. However, the rapid destruction of habitat which is going on in all parts of the country endangers the very existence of those species endemic to Malaysia which are only known from a limited area. For trees, it appears that about half the 600 or so species endemic to Peninsular Malaysia are vulnerable for this reason, while for palms, 20 per cent of 89 endemic species are endangered and only five per cent of all palm species are not threatened.*

Some idea of the danger can be gained from the situation in one small area of 60 hectares of 'enchanted forest' which I was privileged to visit in Sabah. This contains six species of orchid which are not known to occur anywhere else on earth! Its only protection now is the low commercial value of the trees and the poor soil.

By far the worst situation is that of some of the rarest and most beautiful plants growing at or near ground level which have been the victims of thieves who strip every single plant they find to sell, sometimes for enormous prices, to specialist gardeners in wealthy countries. This has led to the near-extinction of spectacular Slipper Orchids and Pitcher Plants (pp.102–3) on Kinabalu, and the disappearance of Slipper Orchids from famous sites in Johor and Langkawi.

---

* The figure for trees from F.S.P. Ng and C.M. Low's "Checklist of Trees of the Malay Peninsula"; palms figure from R. Kiew and J. Dransfield's article in the *Malayan Naturalist*, vol. 41, no. 1, pp. 24–31 (1987).

MOUNTAINS AND LIMESTONE CLIFFS

HIGHLAND VEGETATION

Malaysia has extensive areas over 1,000 metres above sea-level, mostly still forested except for those parts of Cameron Highlands and the Kinabalu foothills where there is cultivation or building. Except for the hill-stations, most of the mountains are little-known because they are inaccessible.

In general temperature falls with increasing altitude by about 0.7°C per 100 metres for small mountains and 0.4°C for large mountains. On small mountains the vegetation zones dependent on altitude are compressed and so the mountain plants grow at lower altitudes. With increasing altitude, besides decreasing temperature, there is increased humidity. The chemical weathering of rocks is slower and soils are more acid, and impoverished by the leaching of nutrients. There is also a greater tendency for the accumulation of peat, resulting in the similarity between mountain forest and lowland heath forest, a similarity which has given rise to much comment.

View from near the summit of Gunung Jerai. The small conifer is Dacrydium beccarii; *the shrub that has just finished flowering under it is* Rhododendron moulmainense, *a species which can be found up to Burma and South China. There is sparse and stunted heath forest on the hill, with ricefields and the sea in the background*

Above the 1,000-metre line the predominant Dipterocarps gradually disappear and the commonest trees are oaks and laurels (Fagaceae and Lauraceae). Higher up, mosses, lichens, liverworts, orchids and other epiphytes may so proliferate as to crowd and shade out the leaves of the trees on which they grow. In this moss forest, or cloud forest as it is sometimes called, the lower parts of the trees may be festooned with mosses and the eye cannot distinguish between solid ground and masses of mosses. On closer inspection, many shrubs in this forest turn out to be epiphytes. A special case is Gunung Api in the Mulu National Park, Sarawak, where alone in Malaysia there are limestone mountains over 1,000 metres high, and the smaller limestone pinnacles in the moss forest are draped in moss and peat, with acid conditions immediately above the alkaline limestone.

Along the tops of many mountain ridges there is a zone, usually quite narrow, of dwarf, stunted trees — an "elfin forest" whose leaves are often small, thick and highly coloured. These leaves are rich in tannins and were thought to be very resistant to decay, but experiments have shown that they decay as quickly as other leaves. Although true heathers are not found here, there is an abundance of members of the Heather family. These include *Rhododendron* (pp.96–7), *Vaccinium* and *Gaultheria* species, which are almost absent from the lowlands.

Native conifers grow in the mountains. These are uncommon in the lowlands except in the heath forests of Borneo but are plentiful on Gunung Jerai (Kedah Peak). There is a dwarf *Dacrydium comosum* forest on Gunung Ulu Kali in the Genting Highlands (p.41), and Kinabalu has 13 species including the extraordinary leafless Celery Pine (p.98), whose terminal branch systems are flattened out and look remarkably like celery leaflets.

Malaysian mountains differ from those of the neighbouring Asean countries in having no native pine trees. There have been efforts to plant them in the uplands as well as the lowlands to produce wood pulp, but these have,

---

Moss forest on Gunung Berincang, Cameron Highlands.

not surprisingly, been disappointing, and much forest has been destroyed.

A few plants growing at sea-level are also found on mountain tops wherever there are roads; these are aliens and have probably spread along the road to the top.

It is surprising to find thick fleshy leaves in what must be one of the dampest habitats in the world (due to the ever-present water vapour in clouds). However, conditions here sometimes promote rapid drying, as when there is strong sunlight and high wind. This is especially true on the high ridges where plants like *Rhododendron ericoides* (p.103), with tiny, long-lasting, needle-like leaves, are found.

It appears that extreme poverty of nutrients in the peaty soil is an important determinant of high mountain vegetation. Thus, near some of the mountain huts on Kinabalu there is an unusual luxuriance of grasses such as the alien *Poa annua*, probably because of enrichment of the soil with urea.

GUNUNG KINABALU

This great mountain, at 4,101 metres, is almost twice as high as any other in Malaysia; it is indeed the highest mountain between the northern tip of Burma and Irian Jaya. Although a young mountain, geologically speaking, it is a refuge for mountain plants which have become extinct elsewhere. It is also a meeting place of plants from different regions. Plants typical of the northern hemisphere include two species each of *Potentilla* and *Gentian*, as well as eight species of *Rubus* (Raspberries and Blackberries) and a Buttercup (p.99). These grow side by side with typical southern hemisphere plants which evolved on the former southern landmass of Gondwanaland. They include the Celery Pine, *Gunnera*, *Trachymene saniculifolia*, at least two species of *Styphelia* (p.105) and *Drapetes ericoides*.

VEGETATION MODIFIED BY MAN

Most of the Malaysian lowland forest has already been logged, and the human impact on vegetation is likely to increase with accelerating development and growing population.

SECONDARY FOREST

When land cleared of its original forest cover is subsequently abandoned, it quickly reverts to forest, but of a very different type from the original primary forest. This secondary forest is known locally as *belukar*.

The vegetation of cleared ground is always unstable and tends to revert to the natural 'climax' vegetation, a process with many, often insuperable obstacles which block or deflect the natural succession of vegetation types. Thus, *belukar* inevitably shows great variations, depending on the nature, duration and timing of previous disturbances, the soil and drainage and the species of tree seeds available.

When, for example, a small clearing made in the forest by shifting cultivators is abandoned after a short period,

conditions are comparatively favourable for regeneration of the original vegetation because of the brief intervention, the lack of damage to the soil by tilling and the availability of seeds of trees with the potential to become emergents. The bare ground may be colonized by a copious growth of ephemeral herbs. There may be giant herbs like wild bananas and gingers, the bamboos, and those trees and shrubs which can sprout from their cut bases. In a matter of months a dense cover of quick-growing, sun-loving saplings may be established. These are the pioneer species; they quickly produce plentiful seed and many of them are short-lived In time shade-tolerant tree species will establish themselves in the shade produced by the pioneers. Ultimately *belukar* comes to look rather like the original forest though lacking the complex stratification of primary forest. The species comprising it are different, too, being far fewer and not as tall, and, generally, Dipterocarps are completely absent.

Native *belukar* trees, which grow naturally in large sunny gaps in primary forest, have long-lasting seeds which are mostly distributed by birds and fruit bats (a few are spread by wind). The presence of seeds already in the soil helps to explain why the trees spring up as soon as conditions become favourable for growth.

Belukar *and, in the background, a few smaller trees of the original forest left after logging. The straight trunk of* Anthocephalus chinensis, *a typical* belukar *tree, is on the left;* Lallang (Imperata cylindrica) *has established itself in front, and wild bananas* (Musa *sp.) can be seen on the right.*

Some crop plants that were cultivated on cleared land may survive its abandonment for decades. Tapioca (p.54) and its shrubby relative *Manihot glaziovii*, Pineapple and the woody twiner *Derris malaccensis* (which was cultivated as an agricultural insecticide) are examples of these. The Para Rubber Tree (*Hevea brasiliensis*)with its explosive fruit capsules is often self-sown near old plantations.

A few alien woody species have established themselves in the *belukar* near settlements and plantations. They include the very aggressive *Acacia auriculiformis*, the African Tulip Tree (p.112), *Paraserianthes (Albizia) falcataria* and the Water Lemon (p.143).

A type of secondary forest which develops after prolonged cultivation on hilly ground has been called "Adinandra belukar" after the most prevalent tree in it — *Adinandra dumosa*. It is common in Johor and may be main-

Vegetation often forms a dense, tangled mass. The Straits Rhododendron (Melastoma malabathricum), a free-flowering shrub with edible berries, is festooned with the very aggressive twining weed Mile-a-minute (Mikania micrantha).

tained by fire. The common components of this type of vegetation are the trees — *Tembusu* (p.115), *Rhodamnia cinerea*, *Myrica esculenta* and *Ploarium alternifolium* — and the shrubs — *Simpoh Air* (p.117) and the Rose Myrtle (*Rhodomyrtus tomentosa*). Three species of Pitcher Plants (p.130) are common too, and there may be dense growth of the scrambling *Resam* ferns. *Belukar* may contain areas overrun by climbers such as *Merremia* spp. (p.133), and some rattans and bamboos.

OPEN GROUND

Malaysia, with its wet climate, has few natural places where there is no tree cover, except for temporary sites such as riverbanks, growing sandy coasts and sites of recent landslides. Other open ground results from the clearing of woodland, fire, cultivation, land reclamation, mining and the construction of roads and buildings. Left to itself, open ground quickly becomes colonized by pioneer tree species so, if an open space remains, there must have been recent interference with this process.

It is easy to tell when there are grazing animals in a *kampung* — the grass is closely cropped. Nowadays, however, the motor mower has supplanted animals as the principal encourager of grasslands in towns and on rural roadsides.

Grasses are well able to withstand close grazing or cutting. The stems of most species creep close to the ground, and the leaves continue to grow from the base when the tops are cut off. When repeatedly cropped, they produce a dense mat of creeping stems and their roots crowd out other herbs, which are usually in the minority except for a short period after the ground has been exposed. Then, the ephemeral weeds of cultivation are usually predominant because their quick-germinating and long-dormant seeds are already in the soil.

Most of the flowering grassland herbs, other than grasses or the similar-looking sedges (*Cyperaceae*), either have low, creeping stems such as the Sensitive Plant (p.122) and Coat Buttons (*Tridax procumbens*), or are too short to be cropped, like some of the smaller, clover-like *Desmodium* species.

Fire is an important destroyer of vegetation. Repeated burning bakes the soil and leads to an impoverished flora of comparatively fire-resistant species. The most important of these is Lallang grass (*Imperata cylindrica*), which covers extensive areas in places with diminished rainfall in Negeri Sembilan, Perak and Sabah. It is highly flammable when dry. A few trees can also withstand fires, probably because of their thick bark. These include the Lallang Tree (*Morinda elliptica*) and *Vitex pinnata*. The Straits Rhododendron survives burning because new branches can sprout from the unburned bases after fire.

Open ground which is grazed occasionally over the years may develop into scrubland, with patches of shrubs, climbers and small trees separated by a network of low grassy cattle tracks. With more intensive grazing there are fewer shrubs, but species distasteful to cattle, such as the Straits Rhododendron, the pungent *Tahi Ayam* (*Lantana camara*), the equally unpleasant herb *Lupang* (*Eupatorium odoratum*) and the camphor-containing herb *Capa* (*Blumea balsamifera*), may persist.

Malay Place Names Based on Trees

Many Malaysian place names are based on the Malay names of trees, showing how important trees were in the people's lives. I found marked on a road map of the Peninsula over 90 places named after trees, but only 11 named after other types of plant. Among the bigger towns are Alur Setar, after the *Setar* tree (*Bouea macrophylla*); Pulau Pinang (Penang), after the *Pinang* palm (p.145); and Ipoh, after the *Ipoh* tree (*Antiaris toxicaria*) from which blowpipe dart poison is extracted. Pahang may have been named after the *Mahang* (*Macaranga* spp.), while Melaka is named after the tree *Phyllanthus (Emblica) offici-*

nalis. Finally Kuala Kangsar means "the rivermouth of the *Kangsar* (*Hibiscus floccosus*)", a forest tree with red-streaked flowers.

Fallen corolla of Kangsar

AGRICULTURAL LANDSCAPE AND CROPS

HUMAN SETTLEMENTS

The population of Peninsular Malaysia is very unevenly distributed. Most of the people live near the west coast, where the principal towns and the agricultural and industrial centres are located. The east coast is sparsely populated except in the rice-growing areas of the Kelantan and Terengganu river basins. Until Independence in 1957, the greater part of the Peninsula was covered with a vast forest, with a few smallholders living along the main rivers and Orang Asli (aborigines), who were mostly shifting cultivators, and a few hundred hunter-gatherers in the forest. This pattern has changed greatly in the last few decades: large areas of land have been cleared for tree crops, and much of the land cleared for short-term cultivation has reverted to *belukar*.

In Sarawak most of the population and the cultivated land are near the coast, with towns mainly located a few kilometres up estuaries in the tidal zone. Further inland the population is sparse, with land often cleared for longhouses and subsistence shifting

cultivation, and permanent plantations of rubber and pepper.

In Sabah the people live mainly on the west coast, where there are a few areas of wet-rice cultivation. The east coast used to have few people, but it now has huge oil palm plantations. Like Sarawak, the interior is sparsely populated by shifting cultivators in most areas, although there are denser populations at Ranau, Tambunan and Keningau with wet rice and dryland crops in the Tenom valley.

THE *KAMPUNG*

The typical Malay *kampung* is a grouping of widely scattered wooden houses. Each house is usually surrounded by fruit trees. Coconuts (p.144) are always present, and the Pinang palm (p.145) is common. Vegetables are not much grown, but there may be giant herbs, like Banana or Papaya, and various useful perennial plants, like the sweet-smelling Pandan (*Pandanus amaryllifolius*), some members of the Ginger family and the shrubby leaf vegetable, *Cekup Manis* (p.138). Further away from the house there may be a smallholding with one or more species of tree crops.

Rubber and cocoa plantations usually produce rather heavy shade; the ground vegetation is likely to be sparse and poor in species especially if weeds

Young rice seedlings are being transplanted into the flooded fields. The foreground shows the grasses and sedges which fringe the padi *field, while behind the fields is the* kampung *land where coconuts and bananas can be seen. The forested hills belong to Pulau Pinang.*

49

have been controlled. Coconut plantations, on the other hand, produce little shade and the light is usually sufficient for a moderate growth of grass and shrubs, except where cocoa is grown underneath.

Kampung plantations in newly settled areas are often surrounded by *belukar* following the growth of a herbaceous crop such as dryland rice, maize or tapioca (p.54).

RICEFIELDS

Flat land with an adequate water supply from a stream, canal or rainwater and a soil rich in clay and fine silt is often converted to the wet cultivation of rice, or *padi* (p.53), using cultivars which need waterlogged soil.

A family from an Iban longhouse in Sarawak watch the burning of their ladang *(forest clearing). In a day or two they will plant* padi *seeds on the land.*

These conditions are also ideal for quick-growing ephemeral water plants (pp.80–3), as well as swamp grasses and sedges (*Cyperus* spp.), which have to be cleared before the new rice crop is planted. The larger canals and sump ponds are often the habitats of the bigger and more permanent water plants such as Waterlilies.

SHIFTING CULTIVATION

This form of cultivation, often called swidden or slash-and-burn, is the predominant form of cultivation in remote rural areas, mainly those inhabited by tribal peoples. A tree-covered area, nowadays usually of *belukar*, is clear-felled and, when dried, the brushwood is burned off, after which the land is planted with dryland *padi* seeds and a few vegetables, a blunt-ended pole or dibbing stick being used to make the holes. After a modest harvest, tapioca is planted, and, a year or so later, the land is abandoned because of pests, weeds and declining fertility.

Shifting cultivation does comparatively little damage to the soil, if it is not continued for too long and if the tree roots are left intact. However, it can only support a sparse population as a large area must be cleared each year, and this has destroyed large quantities of valuable timber. The land gradually regains its fertility but, with increasing population pressure, the carrying capacity of the land is exceeded and younger and younger *belukar* has to be cleared for cultivation, with progressive deterioration of the soil. It is difficult to persuade conservative swidden farmers to change to permanent wet *padi* lands and tree plantations.

HIGHLAND CULTIVATION

In the Cameron Highlands and the foothills of Gunung Kinabalu, there is now widespread intensive cultivation of vegetables, usually on terraced land with generous use of fertilizers and insecticides. Some fruit, such as Mandarin Oranges and Tree Tomatoes (*Cyphomandra betacea*) are also grown. The only plantation crop extensively grown on Cameron Highlands and Sabah is Tea. Delicate crops like Lettuce and ornamentals for the pot plant and cut-flower trade are usually grown under enclosures of transparent plastic, so as to produce blemish-free plants.

TREE CROPS

Malaysian soils are not very fertile and tree crops predominate over herbaceous crops. Instead of breaking up the soil by tillage every year and removing the whole crop, replanting of trees is only needed after several decades. Erosion is greatly diminished by the tree roots in the soil and by the permanent ground cover of leaf litter and undergrowth.

Rubber

Several rubber-producing plant species were brought into Malaysia in the last century, including the India Rubber Tree (p.115), but these have been superceded by the Para Rubber Tree (*Hevea brasiliensis*). The plantation rubber industry was entirely based on the seeds collected in the Amazon basin by Sir Henry Wickham in 1876. Henry N. Ridley in Singapore was responsible for both developing a method of tapping the latex without harming the tree, and encouraging its cultivation. Continuous research, largely by the Rubber Research Institute of Malaysia, has led to increase in productivity of the rubber tree.

In the past, rubber plantations were kept scrupulously free of weeds. A recent development is the growing of a ground cover crop. Seeds of leguminous herbs are planted as soon as the

ground is prepared. These form a dense cover that minimizes erosion while producing nitrogenous fertilizer in their root nodules.

Oil Palms

The oil palm (*Elaeis guineensis*) is the highest yielding producer of vegetable oil — over six tonnes per hectare per year being possible. It produces a moderately unsaturated oil from the fleshy, yellow outer part of the fruit, and small quantities of a more saturated oil from the kernel. It is principally grown in large plantations because it has to be processed quickly in

Ridley found that by making a diagonal cut down to the layer of the latex canals and removing a thin sliver of bark from the lower side of the cut on alternate days, it was possible to have a steady yield of latex without significantly weakening the tree. This is the method of tapping that is still in use.

factories, which have to be large because of economies of scale, before spoilage occurs.

It was brought from West Africa to the Botanic Gardens in Bogor, Java, in 1848, but little was planted in Malaya until the late 1920s. Extensive planting in the last 20 years has resulted in Malaysia producing 65 per cent of the world's crop.

Separate male and female flowers are produced on the same tree. Pollination used to be manually assisted, but recently a pollinating weevil has been introduced. It has done its work so effectively that the resultant heavy crop can overstress the tree! The palms bear fruit after three to four years and are replaced after about 25 years, when harvesting the tall trees becomes difficult.

Robusta coffee (Coffea *cv.) is grown on a modest scale in Malaysia. It is an attractive small tree with fragrant flowers.*

Coconuts

The name comes from the Portuguese *coco*, meaning an imp, from the 'face' on the nut. Coconuts (p.146) are mainly a smallholders' crop near the coast, but they grow just as well inland.

There can be few plants with more uses. The young flowershoot can be made to yield its sap by cutting its surface after bruising. This liquid can be drunk fresh as sweet *toddy* or fermented to produce an alcoholic drink. Kept longer and exposed to the air it produces vinegar, while the fresh juice can be boiled dry to produce the delicious dark brown sugar, *gula melaka*.

Seven months after flowering, the fruit may be plucked and opened for coconut water, a refreshing drink with six per cent sugar. It is sterile, isotonic with human blood and has been used as an intravenous fluid for the treatment of dehydration. The flesh from the more mature fruit is dried to produce copra, which, until 1962, was the major source of vegetable oil in world trade. The residue after pressing out the oil is used as animal feed as it contains nearly 20 per cent protein.

The fruit has a husk, which gives it buoyancy, and it contains a coarse fibre which, in South Asia, is made into doormats and brush bristles. Inside is the shell, one of the hardest vegetable substances known. Craftsmen fashion spoons and containers out of it, and nowadays it is the source of the highest grade charcoal, and is used as a filler for plastics.

Cocoa

Theobroma cacao (p.145) is a new crop in Malaysia, almost unknown until about 15 years ago. It is a small tree of Tropical American origin and it has small, whitish flowers arising from the trunk and main branches. It is planted under the light shade of established coconut plantations or the Mexican Lilac (*Gliricidia sepium*).

When the pods are ripe they are yellow and the seeds rattle inside. The seeds are taken out and fermented for a week, thus killing them and causing the development of the chocolate flavour and a loss of astringency.

Other Tree Crops

Tea (*Camellia sinensis*) used to be grown in lowland Selangor, but the only important plantations now are in Cameron Highlands and Sabah. It can grow 15 metres tall, but it is kept as a flat-topped treelet about 80 centimetres high by hand- or machine-plucking the young shoots every seven to ten days.

Coffee (cultivars developed from *Coffea liberica* and *C. canephora*) is a small tree which is pruned low for easy harvesting of the fruit, each of which contains two seeds (the coffee beans). It is cultivated on a small scale. Two other small trees, Nutmeg (*Myristica fragrans* and Clove (*Eugenia aromatica, E. caryophyllus*), are grown commercially on Pulau Pinang. They are natives of Maluku (the Moluccas or Spice Islands) of East Indonesia.

Sago (*Metroxylon sagu*) is a giant semi-cultivated palm of swampy areas with flowering stems up to 20 metres tall. These are harvested when immature to produce as much as 250 kilogrammes of starch each. This palm is native to East Indonesia and Papua New Guinea, and its leaflets make the best *atap* roofing.

HERBACEOUS CROPS

The continuous cropping of Malaysian soils with herbaceous crops leads to severe erosion and loss of fertility. Wet *padi* is the only important herbaceous crop.

Rice

The rice or *padi* plant (*Oryza sativa*) produces the staple food of almost all Malaysians, and half of the rest of the world too. It probably originated somewhere between India and South China. There are two main methods of growing rice: dryland cultivation is practised by shifting cultivators and on hillslopes, and wet rice cultivation, which is by far the more common method, and is used on terraced slopes.

Wet rice is cultivated in shallow water on flat land. The seeds are first sown in nurseries — in water, floating seedbeds or on dry ground. After a

The hanging ears of padi *are a symbol of fertility, and humility — as kampung people are quick to point out:* "Ikut resmi padi; semakin tunduk, semakin berisi *(Follow the example of the rice plant; the lower its posture, the heavier its yield)."*

month or two, when seedlings have reached a height of 20 centimetres or more and have started to produce side shoots, they are uprooted and the tops are cut off. These seedlings are then planted in the prepared mud lying under a few centimetres of water. (Transplantation saves land, water, weeding, fertilizer and seed, and increases the yield.) The water level in the ricefield is carefully controlled and the fields are gradually dried out before harvest time.

Originally fertilizers were little used as they only made the plants grow taller. Nowadays, however, quick-growing cultivars are grown in large irrigation schemes, notably in Kedah.

Tapioca (Ubi Kayu, Manihot escutenta) *is a large herb which grows freely from pieces of stem stuck in the ground. The tuber contains starch, but the outer part must be discarded to avoid poisoning from hydrocyanic acid.*

They respond well to fertilizers and two good crops are produced a year, but at the cost of harder work, better weed control and more fertilizer.

Compared with dryland herbaceous crops, soil erosion is minimal in wet rice cultivation and cultivation over many years without fallow periods does not exhaust the soil, even when fertilizers are not used.

The only other cereal grown in significant quantities is maize, or *Jagung* (*Zea mais*).

Other Herbaceous Crops

Malaysia is known for its fruits, and several herbaceous fruit plants are grown, including Bananas (*Musa* cvs.) and Papayas (*Carica papaya*). Pineapples (*Ananas comosus*) are grown on a large scale on peaty soil in West Johor.

Other herbaceous crops are grown on a small scale, and these include Tobacco (*Nicotiana tabacum*), which is an important crop in Kelantan, and root crops of Tropical American origin: Tapioca, Sweet Potato or *Keledek* (*Ipomoea batatas*) and Cocoyam or *Keladi Sarawak* (*Xanthosoma sagittifolium*). The native Taro or *Keladi* (*Colocasia esculenta*) is an ancient Indo-Pacific crop, while the Chinese Radish (*Raphanus sativus* var. *longipinnatus*) and several cultivars of *Brassica* (p.138) have been brought from China, where they were domesticated.

Leaf vegetables are intensively cultivated by Chinese smallholders on raised beds and these are heavily manured and watered, thus producing some of the highest yields known in the world. Up to eight crops a year may be produced of several *Brassica* cultivars, also *Bayam* (*Amaranthus gangeticus*), Watercress (*Nasturtium officinale*) and *Kangkung* (*Ipomoea aquatica*; p.23), which also grows wild on the edges of ponds and canals.

Fruit eaten as vegetables include Ladies' Fingers, or *Kacang Buncis* (*Abel-*

moschus esculentus) from Africa, several members of the Bean and Cucumber families, and Eggplants (p.139).

Cultivated climbers include Gambier (*Uncaria gambir*), Tuba (*Derris elliptica* and *D. malaccensis*), all native plants, and Pepper (p.144), which is of Indian origin. Gambier, a hook climber, was once a very important crop grown for its leaves and twigs from which gambier was extracted by boiling. This was used in the tanning and dyeing industries. Tuba is a woody twiner cultivated for its root, which was used to stupefy fish, and is now used as an insecticide.

CONCLUSION

Malaysian agriculture is still based on too few major crop plants, although the spread of the oil palm since the Second World War and the recent introduction of cocoa are welcome changes. In future further advances in the cultivation of hybrid orchids for the cut-flower export industry, and perhaps the development of high-tech, intensive cultivation of specialty crops such as ornamentals, aquarium plants, edible fungi and seaweeds for *agar-agar* (jelly) can be expected.

These farmers' houses in Melaka are set in a grove of coconut and fruit trees. Notice the fine woodwork and the complementary use of potted plants. Several kinds of ornamental plant are grown both in the ground and in pots raised off the ground. These include a Dieffenbachia *and* Croton *cultivars, while hybrid orchids climb up a frame. The atap-and-zinc-roofed houses are kept with meticulous care; the bare ground around them is swept every day.*

ORNAMENTAL PLANTS AND GARDENS

In spite of the thousands of plant species native to Malaysia, few of the plantings by roadsides and in parks and gardens are of native trees. Most natives lack showy flowers and forest trees are difficult establish on hot, dry roadsides. However Yellow Flame (*Peltophorum pterocarpum;* p.61) and Rose of India (*Lagerstroemia speciosa;* p.61) are splendid free-flowering forest natives. *Belukar* trees are easy to establish, but most are unattractive and short-lived. *Tembusu* (p.115) is an exception with cream-coloured flowers and red fruit, while the Wild Cinnamon (p.112) is often planted for its beautiful flushes of young leaves. Two other *belukar* shrubs — the *Simpoh Air* (p.117) and the Straits Rhododendron (p.46) have beautiful flowers, but are so common and familiar that no one thinks of growing them! It would be worth trying out forms of these, or closely related species with extra large flowers, which grow in Sabah, Sarawak and Brunei Darussalam.

Another way of introducing roadside colour is to plant cultivars with multi-coloured leaves, such as Crotons and *Acalypha* species (p.150).

Epiphytes are very common on roadside trees because several common planted trees such as the Rain Tree (*Hujan-hujan; Samanea saman*), Sea Apple (*Jambu Laut; Eugenia grandis*), as well as the Durian (*Durio zibethinus*), support unusually prolific growths of epiphytes. However, only a few species of epiphytes grow in urban sites. These include the Pigeon Orchid (p.134) and several fern species with strap-shaped fronds, of which the Bird's Nest Fern(*Asplenium nidus*) is both common and showy.

Of native free-flowering lianas, only the doubtfully native *Thunbergia grandiflora*, Maiden's Jealousy (*Tristellateia australasiae*) and *Bauhinia kockiana* (p.132) are commonly grown. There are several other striking native Bauhinias which should be brought into cultivation, though seed is scarce and vegetative propagation is difficult.

SHADE AND FOLIAGE PLANTS

Many plants from the tropical forest floor grow well in shady conditions in and around houses, in verandas and car ports, and they are grown for their beautiful leaves, which often have mottled or barred patterns.

An old-established woodland garden in the Waterfall Gardens in Pulau Pinang. The big, buttressed tree is a Kerayong (Parkia javanica), *a close relative of the strong-flavoured* Petai *whose seeds are sometimes cooked in prawn* sambal. *At its foot is a* Dieffenbachia *cultivar, a poisonous herbaceous alien from Tropical America.*

Gardens reflect personal taste, and my personal preference is for gardens which in some way evoke or mimic the natural vegetation of the region. A garden of shade plants of the Arum, Banana, Begonia, Arrowroot and Ginger families, including some giant-leaved herbs together with palms and perhaps bamboos, seems particularly appropriate to Malaysia, and expresses the idea of lush tropical vegetation. There is a scarcity of free-flowering herbs on the forest floor, so it seems right to be sparing with bright colours. The occasional splash of red from *Spathoglottis* (p.149), Busy Lizzies (*Impatiens* cvs.), *Anthurium* cultivars or *Clerodendrum* species (p.153) is enough to evoke the rare patches of brilliant colour in the forest.

ORCHIDS

Orchids from the humid lowlands of the region, mostly hybrids produced by artificial pollination but sometimes also the original species, are the most spectacular and popular cultivated flowers in Malaysia. Most of them are epiphytes in the wild. They can be grown as such on fibre such as coconut husk or tree fern trunk, or on inhospitable, instant-draining material such as charcoal and old broken brick in perforated pots, or on the ground and trained up poles. They hybridize very freely, often even between genera, and are well suited to the climate. Free-flowering hybrids are the basis of a considerable export industry in cut flowers because the blooms can keep their exotic beauty fresh for several weeks in a vase in the cold northern winter.

BULBOUS HERBS AND SUCCULENTS

There are few bulbous plants native to Malaysia, where year-round growth is the rule. Those cultivated are mainly natives of sandy shores and include the native *Crinum* (p.154) and *Sepunoh* (p.66), and the Rain Lilies (*Zephyranthes* spp.) and Spider Lilies (*Hymenocallis* spp.) from Tropical America.

Native succulent species, except for epiphytes, are also few. The thorny-stemmed *Euphorbia antiquorum*, a treelet native to Pulau Langkawi and Perlis, is sometimes grown as a curiosity, and *Kalanchoe pinnata* has escaped to grow wild in sandy places. The beautiful, night-flowering Keng Hwa (*Epiphyllum oxypetalum*) is a cactus from America.

ORNAMENTAL GARDENS

There is so much variety among Malaysian gardens that it is difficult to describe different types, or pinpoint the influence of any particular ethnic group on the gardens of present-day Malaysia. Nevertheless there do seem to be some general patterns.

The Malays

The front of the house may have one or more rows of ornamental plants growing in containers raised on stands or planks, or there may be a screen of shrubby Crotons (p.150). Trailing plants may be grown in baskets hung from the eaves. The earth immediately surrounding the house is swept daily and the footpath leading from the house to the road, or to the river or landing place is kept clear.

The British

It is not surprising that these, perhaps the keenest of all ornamental

A stately home in Georgetown, dating from the 1920s. To the front of the picture there is a clump of Canna *cultivars. To the left can be seen the feathery leaves of the Flame of the Forest* (Delonix regia)*, while in front of the house are Frangipani* (Plumeria *cvs.).*

gardeners, have left their mark on Malaysian gardens. Coming to a world altogether strange to them, they strove to fashion something familiar in their surroundings, like gardens reminiscent of the open parkland which surrounded the stately English country houses.

There was a preference for lawns and colourful flowerbeds, but the grasses were coarse and the flowers, with the exception of Cannas, scanty even though they flowered all the year round. Power and prestige could well be expressed by a splendid curving driveway offering a glimpse of the big house beyond, and local magnates were quick to follow the style. Rubber planters' bungalows and gardens were notable for their beautiful siting, usually on a hillock with a view, as well

A wood-and-'zinc'-roofed Chinese house nestles under the forested hills of Pulau Pinang. It has a colourful 'pot garden' of Bougainvillea cultivars.

as their spaciousness. "Anglo-Malayan" gardens on the grand domestic scale can still be seen in several streets in Georgetown, but only vestiges remain elsewhere, for example in Jalan Ampang, Kuala Lumpur.

Outstanding public gardens of this type are the Istana Besar gardens, Johor Bahru, the Waterfall Gardens, Georgetown and the Lake Gardens in Seremban and Taiping, where mining pools were used to great advantage.

The Chinese

Of the Chinese contribution to gardening, one might mention the wealth of China's flora which has beautified the world's gardens. These include Malaysia's national flower, the Hibiscus (p.155), and the Chrysanthemum. Then there are the open courtyards in front of Chinese temples. Designed to accommodate throngs during festivals,

these offer limited space for plants, which are often grown in containers at the edges of the courtyard.

There is also the art of growing miniature trees and bushes in small pots by limiting root space and constantly pruning and training the branches. This was invented in China, though it is better known by its Japanese name: *bonsai.*

RECENT CHANGES

With the increase in the cost of land and labour, large gardens are becoming rare, except for official and institutional gardening. Houses are now being built with ever smaller gardens, but there is an increased interest in ornamental gardening, at the expense of growing plants with other uses.

The small modern garden has a concrete driveway, quite unnecessarily wide, and a lawn for the children to play on. Often there is an orchid 'house' providing supports for hanging plants, planks for pot plants and a little shade. All this does not take up much space and the local gardener can indulge in the rewarding hobby of orchid growing, once the sole preserve of wealthy hothouse owners in cold climates. The rest of the garden may contain flowering shrubs and a few small fruit trees.

In conclusion, it can be said that most of Malaysia's vegetation has been changed by human activity, and this change can only continue, what with increasing population and accelerating development. It is now becoming more widely understood that human survival everywhere is completely dependent on plants. They are the ultimate source of all our food, and of the oxygen in the air we breathe. They also protect the soil and water supply, and moderate the climate. For these reasons it is very necessary to keep damage to the natural environment due to development to a reasonable minimum, and to monitor the growing environmental impact of the increasing population.

With a rising standard of living and increasing urbanization, people are coming to realize that the enjoyment of plants and gardens, both public and private, is an essential part of civilized life. I hope that this book will play some part in encouraging love and understanding of Malaysia's plant life, so rich, so beautiful and so vulnerable.

Flowering plants are a part of the heritage of Georgetown, Pulau Pinang. Two of Malaysia's most beautiful native flowering trees can be seen here — the Yellow Flame (Kasai; Peltophorum pterocarpum) *in the front and the Rose of India* (Bungor Raya; Lagerstroemia speciosa) *just behind it.*

Overleaf: *How many people will recognize this as a magnified view of our most important food plant, Rice, in full flower? The thread-like filaments carry the cream-coloured anthers which are laden with pollen.*

A reference to a detailed description and the enlargement factor
have been given at the end of each entry, where space permits.
Life-size is represented as: x 1.
The references are abbreviated thus:

FJ   Flora of Java
FM   Flora Malesiana
FMP   The Flora of the Malay Peninsula
FT   Flora of Thailand
HT   Hortus Third
RFM   A Revised Flora of Malaya
TCD   Tropical Crops Dicotyledons
TCM   Tropical Crops Monocotyledons
TFM   Tree Flora of Malaya

Species

1▲

2▲ 3▼

COASTAL AND MANGROVE PLANTS

1   Barringtonia asiatica (Lecythidaceae). **Fish Poison Tree** (Putat Laut or Butun) is a big (15 m.) spreading tree with large, egg-shaped, dark shiny leaves. It grows wild on sandy and rocky shores, and equally well when planted inland. The large, heavily scented flowers open at dusk and are probably pollinated by big moths. Unfortunately the petals and stamens drop at dawn. The fruit are about 10 cm. in diameter, squarish at the base and tapering towards the tip like a truncated pyramid, and contain a large seed. They float and may germinate after drifting great distances. The tree and its seeds contain saponins, and are used as fish poisons.   x 0.3   (TFM,v.2,258)

2   Terminalia catappa (Combretaceae). **Sea Almond** (Ketapang), a native of Indo-Pacific sandy shores, is a favourite tree for roadside plantings. The tree has a very characteristic pagoda shape. Every few months the top of the tree shoots up for a distance of about 3 m. before growth stops. Then several horizontal branches grow out from its top. These have a wavy shape as the end of each branch produces a rosette of leaves, stops growing, then sends a new shoot out from the lower side of the rosette. The leaves turn beautiful colours as they die — red, copper, brown or gold. The seed is an edible nut which is difficult to extract from its flexible, fibrous 'shell', which floats.

x 0.3   (FM,v.4,548)

3   Calophyllum inophyllum (Clusiaceae). **Alexandrine Laurel** (Penaga Laut) can grow up to a height of 20 m., and is sometimes planted by roadsides. The shiny, dark green leaves have numerous small parallel veins and are very tough. The sweet-smelling, short-lasting flowers are followed by poisonous, nearly spherical fruit. The trunk exudes a gum which solidifies, and the seeds contain an oil which was once used for lamps.   x 0.3   (TFM,v.2,186)

4   Memecylon edule (Melastomataceae). Kulit Nipis has thin bark which peels easily. This slightly branched, 11-m.-high shrub grows on rocky and sandy shores. Its fruit is barely edible, in spite of the scientific name. The wood sinks, so it is sometimes used to make anchors. Ridley gives 32 species of this genus in the Peninsula.   x 0.5   (FJ, v.1,374)

5   Guettarda speciosa (Rubiaceae). Selar Makan is a small (9 m.) evergreen shrub of spreading habit which grows on sandy and rocky seashores. Each evening one or two of the fragrant, trumpet-shaped flowers will open. These are pollinated by moths, and the corollas fall off early the next morning. The hard, woody fruits are spherical, about 3 cm. in diameter, and they float.   x 0.3   (FJ,v.2,320)

▲4　▼5

6 **Finlaysonia obovata** (*Asclepiadaceae*). Thi
a woody twiner, with copious milky juice, which gr
in brackish-water estuaries. It has shiny leaves a
unpleasant-smelling flowers.   x 0.5   (FJ,v.2,2

7 **Eurycles amboinensis** (*Amaryllidacea*
Seashore Eurycles (Sepenoh) grows on sandy a
rocky places near the sea, and is common on Pu
Tioman. It has a bulb about 25 cm. by 10 cm. w
and a nearly circular leaf-blade 10 cm. in diameter
a 10-cm. leafstalk. The flowerhead bears about
flowers. Malays and Dyaks consider it to be a pl
with magical properties.   x 0.75   (FJ,v.3,1

8 **Hibiscus tiliaceus** (*Malvaceae*). **Sea Hibis**
(Baru or Baru-baru Laut) is a small (8 m.) tree w
large heart-shaped leaf-blades which are dou
underneath. The corollas are about 8 cm. in diame
open at 9 a.m. and change to a pinkish-brown bef
falling the same evening or the next morning. I
very common and grows wild on dry shores throu
out the tropics. On muddy shores it indicates the bo
dary between the upper limit of salt-water penetrat
and the freshwater swamp. However, it grows q
well when planted inland. The bark contains v
tough fibres used for cordage and for caulking shi
    Another shore tree with similar-looking flower
the Portia Tree (Thespesia populnea). It is ea
recognized by its flattened, globular fruit which
not split when ripe.   x 0.6   (TFM,v.1,3

6▲   7▼

9 Scaevola sericea (S. taccada; *Goodeniaceae*) **Sea Lettuce** (Ambong-ambong) is a 2.5-m.-high rather soft-stemmed shrub of very distinctive appearance which grows at the high tidemark of sand beaches all round the equator. It is the only common member of the family native to SE Asia, though there are many species in Australia. Its fleshy leaves are yellowish-green. The corolla-tube splits along its upper side when the flower opens, and the 5 corolla-lobes are arranged on the lower side. The pithy, oval berries are about 12 mm. long, and they float. A medicinal decoction is produced from the roots in the Philippines. The leaves can be smoked as tobacco.   (FT,v.2,27

The threadlike stems of the Dodder-laurel (Cema
Cassytha filiformis), *a common seaside semi-parasit* can be seen climbing the plant. Its stems are often brownish-red, and its small, round white berries are eaten by birds, thus dispersing the seeds.

x 0.3   (FJ,v.1,135

10 Glochidion littorale (*Euphorbiaceae*). Jamb Kera *(or Selunsor)* is a bushy shrub of sandy shore and, occasionally, mangroves. It grows up to 3 m. i height, and has leathery leaves which turn orange whe old. The flowers are small and green. The fruit has marked dimple at the apex and longitudinal groove It splits from apex to base into 10–15 parts, freeing th orange seeds. The young red leaves are edible.

x 0.17   (FJ,v.1,46

9▲   10▼

11 Cycas rumphii (*Cycadaceae*). The primiti **Seashore Cycad** (Paku Laut) has seeds but no flow ers, and grows wild on dry exposed coasts. It is a palm like shrub with beautiful, dark, shiny fern-like leave and a stout, occasionally branched trunk. Its youn leaves are curled up, like fern tips. It takes hundreds years to reach its full height of about 5 m. The ovule of the female trees are borne on modified leaves and th ripe oval seeds, about 6 cm. long, hang down. Th stamens are borne on spiny scales tightly bunche together to form a cone, like a golden pineapple abou 30 cm. high. The seed is rich in starch, but poisonou as it contains a carcinogen. It was used as famine foo after repeatedly washing the crushed seeds. The so young leaves can be eaten cooked. They are often a tacked by the larvae of blue butterflies (Lycaenidae

The similar-looking C. siamensis grows on th limestone cliffs of Perlis (p.43).   x 0.1   (FT,v.2,18

12 Pandanus odoratissimus (*Pandanaceae* **Common Seashore Screwpine** (Mengkuang Pandan) is a thick-stemmed, 5-m.-high treelet of rock or sandy shores. It has a more branched habit than mo screwpines and rather greyish-blue spine-edged leave The fruit is edible.

P. dubius is a gigantic seashore species with 1 cm.-wide leaves. It grows infrequently on the east coa of the Peninsula, and is sometimes cultivated.

x 0.125   (FJ,v.3,20

13▲ 14▼

13 Ipomoea pes-caprae *ssp.* **brasiliensis** *(Co*
volvulaceae). **Sea Morning Glory** *(Tapak Kuda)*
the most important colonizer of many tropical beach
round the world. Its creeping, rooting stems can for
dense patches which hold down the sand and produ
humus. The leaves vary in shape (pes-caprae mean
goat's foot, while tapak kuda *means horse*
hoofprints). Malays use the juice for fish stings, th
leaves for poultices and the roots are used as
purgative.   x 0.25   (FM,v.4,47*

14 Canavalia maritima *(C. rosea; Papilionaceae*
Greater Sea Bean *(Kacang Laut or Kacang Ran*
rang) is a species which trails on the sandy shore, wh
most of its closest Pea-flower relatives are twiners. T
same is true of the Sea Morning Glory. Its flowers an
young seeds are edible, but care should be taken as th
rather similar seaside twiner, C. microcarpa *(K*
cang Hantu), *with pointed leaflets and inflated pod*
is said to be poisonous.   x 0.4   (FJ,v.1,633;v.3,65*

15 Wedelia biflora *(Asteraceae).* **Sea Oxeye** *(S*
runai Laut) *is a sprawling plant with small, cork*
3-cornered, single-seeded floating fruits, and it grow
on sandy or muddy coasts from Africa to the Pacifi
The leaves are quite variable and are semi-succule
in places where they are exposed to salt spray. Mala
use it for a variety of skin and other diseases and th
young leaves can be eaten, but in small quantitie
because of their diuretic action.

A Caribbean relative, W. trilobata, *with shin*
leaves and orange-yellow flowerheads, is often grow
as it is a lower (20 cm. tall), vigorous, free-flowerin
creeper which quickly covers the ground and can star
both full sun and deep shade.   x 4   (FJ,v.2,404*

16 Catharanthus roseus *(Vinca rosea, Lochner*
rosea; Apocynaceae). **Pink Periwinkle** *(Tahi Ayan*
is a shrubby herb of up to 60 cm. high with wood
stem bases in older plants. Madagascar is thought t
be its country of origin, but some believe it comes fro
the Caribbean. It is common on sandy tropical beach
around the world, and is popular in tropical garder
as it flowers continuously. Sometimes it can be foun
growing rooted in cracks in old buildings. A white
flowered variant is common. Like most members of th
Frangipani family, it is poisonous and, because of it
bitter taste, the plant is avoided by cattle. It contain
many alkaloids. Two of these, vincristine an
vinblastine, are valuable drugs used in the treatmer
of cancer of the embryonic membranes, and acut
leukaemia. They are only present in minute quantitie
— about two parts per million. In Africa and th
Caribbean, it is used as a folk remedy for diabete
mellitus.   x 1.25   (FJ,v.2,228*

▲15 ▼16

71

17▲ 18▼

17 **Cryptocoryne ciliata** *(Araceae). The flowering stem of the **Mangrove Cryptocoryne** (Keladi Laut) is short and the long tubular spathe has coarse fringing hairs. The compound fruit is nearly spherical and splits open to reveal large, green, fleshy, oval seedlings looking like little artificial Christmas trees wrapped in transparent plastic. When shed they float, and the outer covering bursts. The 'branches' of the 'Christmas tree' straighten out and each tree comes to rest on the mud on its flattened base. Roots then grow from the base and leaves develop from the top. This herb grows in brackish water between tidemarks and reaches a height of 50 cm.* (FMP,v.5,86)

Aglaonema griffithii looks rather similar and grows in similar places, but it can be distinguished by its long-stemmed, small greenish flowerhead and oval green, floating fruit. x 0.5 (FJ,v.3,126)

18 **Acanthus ilicifolius** *(Acanthaceae). **Holly leaved Acanthus** (Jeruju Putih) is a stiff, semi-woody plant which grows to a height of 1.5 m. on mud near the high tidemark, sometimes covering large areas. The edges of some leaves bear spines like those of the unrelated European holly and thistle, while other leaves may be almost spineless. The leaves excrete salt, which can be seen as white crystals on the upper side of the leaves after a spell of dry weather. Some botanists have described 3 species; the other two have whitish flowers. This plant has many uses in Malay medicine and was used to ward off evil spirits.* x 0.4 (FJ,v.2,255)

19 **Caulerpa racemosa** *var.* **clavifera** *(Chloro phyta). **Bunch-of-grapes Seaweed** is a creeping edible seaweed found growing on the coral reefs. There are several varieties of this seaweed.* x

20 **Enhalus acoroides** *(Hydrocharitaceae). **Giant Seagrass** (Setul or Jerangau Laut) is the largest of all submarine flowering plants. It grows on protected muddy or coral-sand coasts near the low water tidemark. Leaves, about 1 m. long by 2 cm. wide, grow from a buried rhizome covered with stiff black fibres. Male and female flowers are on different plants and mature when low-water spring tides occur at about 4 p.m. Male plants (as shown here) produce large numbers of small white flowers which blow freely over the water when their hairlike stalks break. Both the male and the larger, green, 3-petalled female flowers float as they have water-repellent surfaces. The developing fruit — which is edible and squishy like the seeds of a cucumber — is brought to the sea bottom by its stem which becomes tightly coiled as the fruit matures.* x 2 (FM,v.5,402)

21 Rhizophora mucronata *(Rhizophoraceae). T*
Mangrove Tree (Bakau Kurap) *is about 20 m. hig*
when fully grown. Its small greenish-cream flowe
develop into seedlings with pointed root-shoots up
60 cm. long. In the picture they are seen hanging fro
the branches like javelins. When these fall, they flo
away or stick in the mud and put out lateral roots fro
near their lower end.

The species lower down, with narrow leaves an
small 'javelins', is Kandelia candel (Berus-berus
a small tree with buttress roots. The flowers of bot
species are visible. x 0.1 (FM,v.5,452

22 Lumnitzera littorea *(L. coccinea; Combre*
taceae). The beautiful **Red Teruntum** *flowers whe*
quite young. It has shiny, fleshy leaves and grows o
firmer, better-drained shores than those favoured b
most mangrove species. The related species, whic
is shorter (6 m. tall) and has white petals, is L. race
mosa. It has very hard wood. x 0.5 (FM,v.4,586

23 Acrostichum aureum *(Dennstaedtiaceae). Th*
3-m.-tall **Giant Mangrove Fern** *(Piai Raya) grow*
in mangrove throughout the tropics. It is found on th
upper part of the foreshore up to the spring tide high
water mark. It can survive in freshwater and can mak
an impressive ornamental. The young shoots are edible
while Malays make a paste of its rootstocks for healin
wounds and boils. In Vietnam the leaflets are used t
thatch roofs. x 0.07 (RFM,v.2,409

21▲ 22▼

24▲ 25▼

24 Dolichandrone spathacea *(Bignoniaceae). T* ***Mangrove Trumpet Tree*** *(Tui or Tuai) is fai* *common in a variety of brackish to freshwater habit* *ranging from tidal reaches of rivers to sandy beaches.* *Perlis it is often found growing by the roadside in pa* *growing areas, where it has a generally pyramic* *form, with one or several sinuous, upright main branch* *and short horizontal branches. Further south this 1* *m.-tall tree shows a broader, less distinctive shape. F* *fragrant flowers open in the evening and usually f* *early the next morning. Since the corolla tubes are* *cm. long, pollination must be by very large moths. T* *seeds have corky wings and are water-borne.*

x 0.6   (FJ,v.2,54

25 Derris heterophylla *(D. uliginosa; Papilio* *aceae). As its name suggests,* ***Three-leaved Sea Derr*** *(Akar Ketuil) is a woody twiner with 3-5 leaflets.* *grows in mangrove and has single-seeded round pod* *Other species — D. elliptica and D. malaccens* *(Tuba) — were used as fish poisons and are valuab* *insecticides because they contain rotenone.*

x 0.6   (FMP,v.1,59

26 Nypa fruticans *(Arecaceae). The beautiful* ***Nip*** ***Palm*** *is quite unlike any other palm. It is fou* *growing between tidemarks up estuaries where there* *a considerable mixture with freshwater. Its thick ste* *creeps on the surface of the mud, occasionally dividir* *into two, while its leaves (see picture on p.17) mc* *reach heights of 10 m. The floating fruits, often with* *shoot emerging, can survive for many months. Nip* *has many uses. Young leaves make cigarette wrapper* *while old ones are used as thatch (atap). The sweet, so* *gelatinous fruit is eaten and the sap from the flowe* *stem contains 17% sugar. In Sarawak, salt was extracte* *from the ashed stems. There is only one species in th* *genus and fossilized fruits, indistinguishable fror* *present-day fruits, have been found in London clay.* *The picture shows the flowerheads, with mainl* *male flowers. Part of the spherical cluster of femal* *flowers, protected by bracts, can be seen in the left c* *the picture.*   x 0.6   (FJ,v.3,199

27 *(following double page)* **Sonneratia caseolari** *(S. acida; Sonneratiaceae). Beremban (or Pedada* *often lines tidal riverbanks as far as salt water penetrates* *and this 20-.m.-tall tree can survive in freshwater. It* *aerial roots project like sharp cones from the mud an* *are so light that fishermen use them for floats. Th* *spectacular flowers open at night and are pollinated b* *pollen-eating bats. The stamens fall off the next morn* *ing. The flattened, spherical fruit contains many smai* *seeds which are acid, but edible. The proboscis monke* *of Borneo is dependent on young Sonneratia shoots* *while the gregarious Pteroptyx firefly prefers to us* *this tree for its permanent nocturnal displays. Suc* *firefly trees were preserved as aids to navigation or* *the Perak River.*   x 3   (FJ,v.2,258

SWAMPFOREST AND WATER PLANTS

28▲

29▲ 30▼

28 Eichhornia crassipes (*Pontederiaceae*). **Water Hyacinth** (Keladi Bunting) *was introduced from Brazil early in this century. It is now a serious pest in most tropical countries, covering large areas of quiet fresh water, interfering with navigation and shading out other plants. In Malaysia it is often cultivated as pig food. It has no local enemies except man, and is the only large herb (30 cm. high) which floats on the water surface unattached to the bottom. It is buoyed by its swollen, spongy leafstalks. The ash is a rich source of potassium.*   x 0.3   (FM,v.4,259)

29 Limnocharis flava (*Butomaceae*). **Yellow Bur head** (Jinjir) *is a native of S. America, but it is now common in ricefields. Like many marsh plants it has soft, fleshy leaves and air-containing stems. It is rooted in the mud, and reaches a height of 60 cm. Leaves and flowers are edible.*   x 0.25   (FJ,v.3,2)

30 Nymphoides indica (Limnanthemum indi cum; *Gentianaceae*). *The* **Water Gentian** *is a dainty plant, and only the flowers are raised above water. Its floating leaf-blades resemble those of a small waterlily, but they have short leaf stems attached to long stalks anchored in the mud. The stems break easily and plantlets, each with a single leaf and numerous flowers, can float away to take root elsewhere.*

x 0.6   (FJ,v.2,441)

31 Nelumbo nucifera (Nelumbium nelumbo; *Nymphaeaceae*). *Unlike the related Waterlilies, the* **Sacred Lotus** *(Teratai or Seroja) has long, blunt spined flower- and leafstalks which are usually raised up to about 1 m. above water level, and the leafstalk is attached near the middle of the leaf-blade. It is especially sacred to Buddhists, to whom the flower represents the perpetual cycles of reincarnation. The pink or white flowers open in the morning and the petals fall in the afternoon. The seed-like fruits are embedded in pits on the flat top of the conical receptacle. They are eaten raw, when unripe, or cooked, when ripe, after the bitter embryo has been removed. The hollow starchy rhizomes are formed like a string of sausages, and are boiled or candied and eaten. Young leaves and leafstalks can be eaten, while the leaf-blades are used to wrap food, and contain a milky juice. In Malaysia the Lotus grows throughout the year, but where there is a distinct cold or dry season, it has a period of dormancy. Its seeds can germinate after centuries.*

The Waterlilies (Telipok) include the small, wild cream-coloured Nymphaea stellata, and cultivars of the night-opening red, pink or white N. lotus, and the day-opening blue N. capensis.   x 0.5   (FJ,v.1,148)

32 **Ludwigia adscendens** (Jussiaea repens; Ona graceae). **Water Primrose** is a floating plant wit shiny, deep green leaves that have pale veins. It common in Malaysia in shallow stagnant water and c exposed mud, and occurs from India to New Guinea. puts out long hollow stems on the water surface, and further buoyed by spindle-shaped floats, which ar modified roots; these only develop when the plant growing on water. When growing on mud it has down leaves and shorter stems without floats and flowers.

There are several species in Malaysia which ar upright marsh plants having 4-petalled yellow flower. Some of them produce filmsy white breathing root whose tips float to the surface, when growing in mu

x 1

33 **Cryptocoryne cordata** (Araceae). There ar nearly 50 species of Cryptocoryne in SE Asia. A. but one (p.72) grow firmly rooted to the bottom c freshwater forest streams. **Water Trumpets** (Kelad Paya) are in great demand for tropical aquaria becaus their leaves are often beautifully mottled, and the tolerate deep shade. The spathe is rolled up into watertight tube. Insects crawl down this tube to th distended lower end, which is below water level, an pollinate the small flowers arranged around a shor central column. This species was photographed i S. Johor.   x 0.75   (FMP,v.5,8

32▲ 33▼

34 **Utricularia aurea** (U. flexuosa; Lentibula riaceae). **Golden Bladderwort** is a common, car nivorous plant which floats unattached in stagnar water. Most of the plant is submerged, only the 15 cr flowering stem projecting above water. It has group of feathery, subdivided leaves (there is some doub whether these are true leaves, or stems) bearing blac ders 2–3 mm. long. Each bladder is flattened and close by a 'door'. When a minute aquatic animal knock against a hair on the 'door', it opens and water is sucke into the bladder, together with the animal. There ar about 15 species of Bladderwort in the Peninsula, ar many of these are found in marshy places, wit undissected leaves, and bladders borne on separa stems.   x 0.75   (FJ,v.2,51

35 **Ottelia alismoides** (Hydrocharitaceae). **Turtl Grass** (Keladi Air) is another submerged plant, but is rooted in the mud of ponds and ditches. Only th flowers are borne above water. These have 3 petals an are sometimes pale pink. Turtle Grass is widely disperse throughout the Asian tropics. It is common in Keda and Pulau Pinang, but does not seem to grow well i the south of the Peninsula. It is eaten in Peninsula Thailand and the Philippines.   x 0.75   (FJ,v.3,

36 Horsfieldia irya *(Myristicaceae).* Lempoya Paya *(or* Pianggu) *is a narrow, 25-m.-tall tree swampforest and ricefield, but it also grows well well-drained forests. It produces aerial knee-root especially when growing in tidal areas. The droopi branches bear two rows of leaves. The tiny, unisexue spherical flowers only open slightly, but have a deligh ful penetrating fragrance. The globular fruit are abo 2.5 cm. in diameter, and turn pinkish-orange.*

x 0.3　(TFM,v.1,32

37 Ixora lobbii *var.* **stenophylla** (I. stenophyll *Rubiaceae).* This Ixora *is a shrub which grows c riverbanks in Johor, Pahang and Borneo. It reaches height of about 2 m. and is able to survive whe submerged by torrential floodwaters. Typical of su rheophytes are its long, narrow and shiny leaves. I flowers are much larger than those of other Ixoras.*

x 0.5　(FMP,v.2,9

38 Dysoxylum angustifolium *(Meliaceae). Th* **River Dysoxylum** (Kamanju) *is a 5-m.-high shru which lines riverbanks, often in association with* Nera *(p.28). It is a typical rheophyte with narrow leather leaflets. The whitish flowers smell of garlic, and th fruit (shown here) fall in the water and are eaten by fis Thus the fruit are sometimes used as fish bait. Corn reports that fish become poisonous to man during th fruiting season.* x 0.5　(FMP,v.1,39

36▲　37▼

FOREST PLANTS

39 Dysoxylum cauliflorum *(Meliaceae). T[?]
cream-coloured, scented flowers of* **Stem Dysoxylu[?]**
*(Balun Hijau) are produced on short stems issui[?]
from the tree trunk. These develop to produce t[?]
orange fruit with black seeds. The waxy pulp su[?]
rounding the seeds is said to be edible. Early botanis[?]
thought that these belonged to a parasite growing [?]
the tree. The prominent breathing pores can be se[?]
on the trunk.* x 0.2   (FMP,v.1,39[?]

40 Cratoxylum formosum *(Hypericaceae).* **Pir[?]
Mempat** *is easily distinguished from the other fore[?]
trees when in flower. Once or twice a year, the lea[?]
fall and flowers are borne among the red-tinged ne[?]
leaves. Individual flowers open two hours after dav[?]
and close that afternoon. Unfortunately floweri[?]
only lasts 2–3 days. The 10-m.-tall tree is sometim[?]
denuded by the caterpillars of butterflies of the gene[?]*
Neptis *and* Lassipa. x 0.67   (TFM,v.2,25[?]

41 Shorea macroptera *(Dipterocarpaceae).* M[?]
lantai *(or* Kepung) *has fruits with 3 large wing[?]
which are enlarged sepals. They cause the fruit to sp[?]
when it falls, but as it is rather heavy, it is not blou[?]
far by the wind. The bark of the tree can be used f[?]
house walls, and the timber of this, and others of th[?]
genus, is known as red meranti.* x 0.6   (FM,v.9,53[?]

39▲   40▼

42

42 Globba *sp.* *(Zingiberaceae). Globbas (Halia Hu tan) are small, non-aromatic members of the Ginge family growing on the forest floor. They have stem which bend over and bear leaves in two rows. Th flowerheads have colourful bracts and often hav tuberous bulbils, which fall off and reproduc vegetatively. The plant illustrated is from Pulau Pinang and there are about 10 species in the Peninsula.*

x 0.

43 Sonerila heterophylla *(Melastomataceae There are some 40 species of* Sonerila *native t Peninsular Malaysia, of which 35 are endemic. Mos of them grow on the forest floor in the lowlands and u to 900 m. altitude. This attractive species, know locally as* Ati-ati Gajah, *is found from Johor to Pera and in Borneo and Sumatera. Efforts should obviousl be made to bring it into cultivation.*

Another similar species is S. picta. *It has marble or veined white patterns on the upper side of the leaves*

x 0.6   (FMP,v.1,785

43 ▲   44 ▼

44 Thottea *sp.* *(Aristolochiaceae). Thotteas ar hard-stemmed plants with large oval leaves. The flower of this species issue from the base of the stems. The mos visible part of the flowers are their 3 sepals. Thottea seem to be scentless, although some of them have th dull red flowers characteristic of carrion flowers, whic attract flies (p.95). They are also the host plant fo caterpillars of some beautiful Swallowtail butterflies*

The species shown here was recently discovered b a butterfly collector in a small surviving patch o belukar near the centre of a town in Perak, as Swallowtail alighted on its leaves to lay its eggs. It is one of 3 newly discovered species in Malaysia, as ye unnamed. It shows that there may yet be a wealth o undiscovered plants in the country. Such plants ar threatened with extinction.

45 Dipterocarpus grandiflorus *(Dipterocar paceae).* Dipterocarp, *in Greek, means two-winge fruit, and most members of this family have winge fruits, but usually with more than two wings. This Dipterocarp* (Keruing Belimbing) *is a very widel distributed, from the Andamans to the Philippines and is found throughout Malaysia and Brune Darussalam.*

Decomposing leaf litter can be seen between the fallen leaves. Plant nutrients are being liberated an many tree rootlets grow in this region, and some ar exposed (top right).   x 0.8   (FM,v.9,317

46 **Didymocarpus platypus** *(Gesneriaceae). Th∎ Broad-leaved Didymocarpus* (Julong Rimba ∎ Semboyen) *is a rather woody-stemmed perennial he∎ which grows on the forest floor. It is about 75 cm. hig∎ with a crown of hairy leaves and it flowers profuse∎ but infrequently.*

There are over 53 species of Didymocarpus *in th∎ Peninsula, 46 of which are endemic (p.97 shows ∎ mountain species). Malays use a decoction of the roo∎ for treating coughs.*   x 0.25   (FMP,v.2,517

47 **Tacca integrifolia** *(T. cristata; Taccaceae). T∎ flowering stem of the Black Lily* (Keladi Mura∎ *bears a series of purplish-black flowers with outwardl∎ curved petals and sepals. The flowerhead is surrounde∎ by 3 sets of bracts. The outermost two bracts, one abo∎ and one below, are broad and purple (not shown in th∎ photograph). Inside this are two long, narrow, uprigh∎ bracts forming a hood over the flowers. The innermo∎ bracts are the numerous white hanging threads. T∎ whole plant is about 70 cm. tall.*

The related T. leontopetaloides *is Tahiti Arro∎ root. Its starchy tubers need repeated washing to g∎ out the bitterness before they can be eaten. It grows wi∎ on sandy coasts.*   x 0.3   (FM,v.7,809–11

48 **Dracaena aurantiaca** *(Agavaceae). This Dr∎ caena is a beautiful shrub about 3 m. tall, and it wou∎ be worth cultivating for its mottled leaves, which a∎ purple when young. It has few, rather upright, sem∎ woody stems and bears spherical orange fruit abo∎ 2 cm. in diameter.*

There are about 20 native species of Dracaena ∎ *the Peninsula, including* D. maingayi *which is ∎ forest tree growing up to 20 m. tall. Several exot∎ species are cultivated as foliage plants; some tolera∎ deep indoor shade. Dracenas take root readily fro∎ pieces of stem.*   x 0.3   (FMP,v.4,33∎

49 **Musa violascens** *(Musaceae). This small, 2-m∎ high Banana* (Pisang) *has the erect flower spik∎ characteristic of bird-pollinated bananas, with on∎ flower per bract. It is endemic to Perak, Negeri Sembila∎ Selangor and Pahang, and may be seen beside the ol∎ Kuala Lumpur–Pahang road.*

Malaysian wild bananas are easily identifie∎ M. gracilis *is similar to* M. violascens, *but has ∎ spindle-shaped flowerhead with two flowers per brac∎ It is only known from Terengganu, Endau–Rompin ∎ Pahang, Johor and Melaka. The other wild banana∎* M. acuminata *and* M. truncata, *are several metre∎ tall, and they occur all over the Peninsula except in th∎ south. They have hanging flowerheads.*   x 0.1

50 **Geodorum citrinum** *(Orchidaceae). This bea∎ tiful little (10 cm.) ground orchid has unusually bro∎ leaves. It is most commonly found in the north of th∎ Peninsula and in Burma and Thailand.*

            x 1   (RFM,v.1,53∎

46▲ 47▼

51 Zingiber spectabile (*Zingiberaceae*). The **Blac Gingerwort** (Tepus Tanah or Cacak) has flowerhead (illustrated) which issue from a short thick rhizom The fleshy bracts, which turn red when old, contain watery fluid with a faint aromatic taste. A flowe develops at the axil of each bract, but this lasts only few hours. The stems are about 2 m. high and have tw rows of leaves on the upper part. x 0.5 (FMP,v.4,25

52 Achasma macrocheilos (*Zingiberaceae*). **Ye low Earth Ginger** (Tepus Tanah) is a typical larg ginger with edible stems up to 6 m. tall. The flowerhead are partly hidden underground and may be som distance from the stems of the plant. The specimen i the photograph has 7 flowers. The lips of the flower from different plants are very variable in colour. Som botanists recognize a very similar ginger with almos all-scarlet flowers as a distinct species — A megalocheilos. x 1 (FMP,v.4,270

53 Hornstedtia scyphifera (*Zingiberaceae*). **Grea Spindle Ginger** (Tepus) is a ginger with a growt habit similar to that of other large gingers, havin stems up to 5 m. tall. The rhizomes typically grov slightly above ground level, supported by stilt-roots The flowerhead is borne on a short stalk and enclosed i a spindle-shaped series of overlapping mottled bract with tubular flowers issuing from the top of the spindle Hornstedtias are cultivated in Java for their leaves an fruits, which are used as flavourings. x 0.6

51▲ 52▼

54 Nepenthes bicalcarata (*Nepenthaceae*). **Two-spurred Pitcher Plant** *is a lowland species found only in peaty swamps in Borneo. It is remarkable because of the two thorns under the lid which stick into the mouth of the pitcher. The other remarkable feature is that it is an ant plant. The ants live in a hollow swelling where the tendril joins the pitcher. (See pp.100-1,130 for more pitcher plants.)* x 1

55 Thismia arachnites (*Thismiaceae*). *This delicate, fleshy plant contains no chlorophyll, and so does not make its own food. Instead, it derives its nutrition from dead vegetation in the way fungi do. It has thick worm-like roots.* x 1.5 (FM,v.4,24)

56 Rafflesia pricei (*Rafflesiaceae*). *Rafflesias are only found in SE Asia. For much of its life the plant is invisible as it consists of a highly specialized set of absorbtive organs within the bases of the stems of lianas* (Tetrastigma *spp.). The hard flowerbud bursts through the bark of the host plant and develops as a slightly flattened brown spherical mass (bottom left in picture). It finally opens to reveal a cauldron-shaped corolla. It is a carrion flower, looking and smelling like rotting meat, and is pollinated by flies.*

This species is found only in Sabah. Other species of Rafflesia *include* R. hasseltii, *found in Perak, and the largest of the genus,* R. arnoldii, *which is confined to Sumatera. It is the largest flower in the world.*

54▲ 55▼

MOUNTAIN PLANTS

57▲

58▲ 59▼

57 Medinilla clarkei *(Melastomataceae). Th*
small (70 cm.) shrub with rather fleshy leaves i
common on Cameron Highlands and Bukit Fraser
Although it looks like an ordinary shrub, close
investigation shows that this and other Medinillas ar
usually epiphytes, attached to the lower part of a tree
which may be covered in moss. Ridley reports 1
species in the Peninsula, of which 6 are endemic.

The showy M. speciosa *is another epiphytic shru*
which grows in the mountains. It has pink flower
heads with pink sepals, petals and flower stems, whi
M. scortechinii *has scarlet flowerheads.*

x 0.6   (FMP,v.1,80?

58 Cyrtandra clarkei *(Gesneriaceae). This 50-cm*
high herb has dark green leaves covered with silk
silvery hairs. It grows on Kinabalu at an altitude
about 2,500 m.   x 0

59 Aeschynanthus speciosa *(Gesneriaceae). Th*
stout shrubby **Lipstick Plant** *is one of about a doze*
species in this genus in Peninsular Malaysia. It ca
also be found in Borneo, where this photograph w
taken. It grows to a height of about 50 cm.

Most Aeschynanthus *are epiphytes in the mour*
tains, but there are some lowland species. Several a
cultivated as hanging basket plants, and one of thes
from Genting Highlands, was awarded a Banksi
Medal by the Royal Horticultural Society of Londo
a prize only given to ornamental plants of distinctio
x 0.6   (FMP,v.2,49?

60 *(left)* **Didymocarpus hirtus** *(Gesneriaceae) a*
(right) **Sonerila rudis** *(Melastomataceae). The*
plants were photographed on a shady bank in t
Cameron Highlands at about 1,900 m. elevatio
Didymocarpus *is a very variable creeper. Most of t*
species in this genus in the Peninsula grow in t
mountains. A lowland Didymocarpus *species is fe*
tured on p.90, while a lowland Sonerila *species is o*
p.88.   x 0.6   (FMP,v.2,515; v.1,78?

61 Pratia (Lobelia) begoniaefolia *(Campan*
aceae). This small creeper roots at the nodes a
sometimes forms a dense mat on the ground. The r
berries are spongy and tasteless. It is common
Cameron Highlands and Bukit Fraser, and is found
far north as China.

Pratia (Lobelia) montana, *which is found on t*
mountains in Peninsular Malaysia, and Pratia (L
belia) borneensis, *which grows on Kinabalu, ha*
similar but larger flowers and a ridged, dry fru
However, they are rather straggly, upright herbs.
x 1   (FMP,v.2,20

▲60　▼61

62 Lycopodium complanatum (L. platyrhiz
ma; *Lycopodiaceae*). This **Club-moss** has long cree
ing stems from which arise short upright ster
terminating in club-shaped cones. These cones have
spore-bearing organ on the upper surface of each
its leaf-like scales. It was photographed on Gunu
Berincang, and may be 20 cm. tall.

The pale grey tufts at the right in the photogra
are Fruticose (Shrubby) Lichens. Lichens are ve
slow-growing, composite plants formed from two ve
different kinds of plant: a fungus, which provides t
mechanical support, lives symbiotically with a sing
celled alga that carries out photosynthesis.   x (

63 (*left*) **Podocarpus imbricatus** and (*righ
Phyllocladus hypophyllus (*Podocarpaceae*). Tv
young conifers are illustrated: P. imbricatus (Cuc
Atap) can grow into a 30-m.-tall tree. Its leaves a
of two sorts: long leaves about 1 cm. long closely a
ranged on short stems, giving the superficial appea
ance of a pinnate leaf, and short needles arranged rou
the branches. There are 6 species of Podocarpus
Peninsular Malaysia.   (TFM,v.2,2C

The Celery Pine (P. hypophyllus) has flat, celer
like "leaves", which are actually modified stems,
phylloclades, a primitive feature similar to those
prehistoric non-flowering trees. Seeds and pollen a

62▲   63▼

84 Cinnamomum iners (*Lauraceae*). A quick growing small tree up to about 10 m. high, **Wild Cinnamon** (Kayu Manis Hutan or Medang Teja) is often planted by roadsides for the brightly coloured new leaves which it puts out at frequent intervals. Its small yellowish flowers have an unpleasant waxy smell. The small black fruits are eaten by birds, squirrels and fruit bats, thus dispersing the seeds. The leaves smell faintly of cinnamon and are eaten by caterpillars of the Blue-bottle Butterfly. x 0.25 (FJ,v.1,120)

85 Spathodea campanulata (*Bignoniaceae*). The **African Tulip Tree** is about 20 m. tall, grows quickly and has two-winged, air-borne seeds which germinate freely. It is common around towns. The flowerbuds are filled with liquid — natural water-pistols when squeezed — and the bird-pollinated flowers last several days. The canoe-shaped dry fruit are about 25 cm. long and split lengthwise. Its shallow roots make this tree unsuitable for roadside planting. x 0.5 (FM,v.8,185)

86 Macaranga hypoleuca (*Euphorbiaceae*). Mahang Putih (or Balik Angin) is one of the 27 species of Macaranga in Malaysia, and it is common in disturbed, well-lit sites. It has blue-green waxy stems and three-lobed leaf-blades with hollow, ant-inhabited twigs. It produces tiny, green, wind-pollinated flowers. In the illustration, the ants are feeding on the white starchy food-bodies produced by the plant. x 1 (FJ,v.1,488)

84▲ 85▼

4 Cassia alata *(Caesalpiniaceae). A native of tropical America,* **Seven Golden Candlesticks** *(Ge-*enggang*) may have come to Malaysia via the Philippines, as suggested by its Filippino name, Acapulco – the Mexican port of departure of the Manila galleon. This treelet commonly grows wild in disturbed damp places, such as floodplains. It is short-lived, with few, rather coarse branches and it grows to a height of 3 m. The flowerbuds are covered with orange bracts which fall when the flower opens. The leaves are used to treat fungal skin infections. They contain chrysophanic acid, a fungicide. The seeds are small and square, and rattle softly when the winged pod is shaken. They are purgative and vermifuge.* x 0.05   (FJ,v.1,540)

5 Dillenia suffruticosa *(Dilleniaceae).* **Shrubby Dillenia** *(Simpoh Air) grows up to 5 m. in height and has very characteristic cabbage-like, oval leaves which are slightly toothed and up to 35 cm. long. These are often used to wrap food. The red fruits open before dawn into several segments, exposing the red-fleshed, seemingly tasteless seeds which are so attractive to birds that they are usually eaten before we get the chance to see them. This swampforest shrub roots freely from low branches and it is a successful colonist of dry, eroded hillsides. It makes an ideal ornamental, and there are similar species of* Dillenia *with extremely large flowers in NE Sarawak. These could be experimented with for gardening.* x 0.4   (TFM,v.1,192)

▲94   ▼95

96 ▲

97 ▲   98 ▼

96 Mimosa sepiaria *(Mimosaceae).* **Giant M** *mosa is a straggling shrub up to 9 m. tall. It is* Tropical American native and is common on wastelan *The plant bears numerous thorns, which are flattene like rose thorns, and these are often reddish in colou as may be the leafstalks and twigs.*

Two other relatives also found on wasteland ai M. pigra *and* M. invisa. *Both are like* M. pudic *(p.126) in having sensitive leaflets, but they droc slowly when shaken. The first is a short-lived, thorn flat-topped treelet of about 4 m. high which has maw flowerheads and spreading branches.* M. invisa *scran bles to a height of 1.5 m. It is herbaceous, sometime woody, and bears pink flowerheads.* x C

97 Cananga odorata (Canangium odoratum; A; nonaceae). Kenanga *has a characteristic pole-like trun which often bends over at the top. The tree has a spar. irregular crown with branches hanging down at th tips. The flowers are green when immature and the become yellow and fragrant. There appears to be tu forms, the wild one occurs in the northern part of th Peninsula while the other, with a superior scent, planted in villages. It is cultivated in some countries fe the ylang-ylang oil in the flowers.*

There is also a sterile, dwarf variety, C. odorat var. fruticosa. *This probably came from Thailand an is often planted in gardens, where it grows to a heigh of a few metres. It has narrow, curly petals.*

x 0.5   (FJ,v.1,10!

98 Mussaenda frondosa *var.* **glabra** *(Rubiaceae* This **Mussaenda** (Balek Adap *or* Adap-adap) *is woody scrambler up to 3 m. high often seen climbing b the roadside. It is instantly identifiable by its occasiona showy white 'leaves', which are really greatly-expande calyx-lobes. There are two types of flower, both produc seeds but only one produces pollen.*

Another wild species, but without the enlarge sepals, is M. mutabilis, *with orange star-shaped cc rollas 4 cm. in diameter. Exotic species cultivated fc their showy calyx-lobes include* M. philippica *fror the Philippines, which is the most common, with sever cultivars having bunches of white or pink calyx-lobe and reduced flowers; the African* M. flava, *with yellov flowers and cream-coloured calyx-lobes, and cultivar derived from* M. erythrophylla *(Ashanti Blood), wit red calyx-lobes.* x 0.5   (FJ,v.2,30·

99 Caladium bicolor *(Araceae). Originally intro duced from S. America because of their beautifu coloured leaves,* **Caladiums** *have escaped and are no wild in rubber estates. Many cultivars with brightl; coloured and strikingly-patterned leaves have bee developed by nurserymen from the original wild typ which has small red and white blotches on the leaves The flowerhead with its cream-coloured spathe is nc very commonly seen. The plant is propagated by tuber and sometimes the leaves die down for several month; especially during dry periods.* x 0.5   (FJ,v.3,12;

100 **Amorphophallus campanulatus** *(Aracea*
Elephant-foot Yam (Loki) *is a giant herb with 2-m*
high purple-mottled leafstalks and much-divided lea
blades. After the leaves have died down, the mul
coloured flowerhead emerges, with thick bell-shap
spathe enclosing a short wrinkled spadix bearing m
nute flowers. It smells of rotting flesh and is pollinat
by carrion flies. The stalk lengthens after flowerir
and bears numerous small fruit. The young leaves c
be eaten after thorough boiling. It is common in op
and slightly shady places, especially in the north. Wi
forms of this plant contain numerous needle-like cryst
of calcium oxalate and a poisonous alkaloid. Howeve
they are said to be edible after washing and prolong
boiling. Edible varieties cultivated in Java and Ind
can produce a tuber weighing 25 kg. within a year –
enough to feed a family for a week!

x 0.25   (FJ,v.3,11

101 **Laurentia longiflora** (Isotoma longiflor*
Campanulaceae). **Star of Bethlehem** *is a native*
Tropical America from Florida to Peru, and it we
introduced as an ornamental, but is now most common
ly found growing wild in moist, shady places nea
human settlements. It has a poisonous, acrid, milk
juice and a drop of this is said to be able to produc
blindness. Even the copious nectar at the base of th
long corolla-tube has an unpleasant peppery taste. Th

100▲ 101▼

plant is said to contain alkaloids which cause paralysis.
x1 (FM,v.6,140)

102 Turnera ulmifolia *(Turneraceae).* **Yellow Turnera** *(or Holy Rose) is a herb with a woody stem base and it reaches a height of nearly 1 m. It grows wild in dry places, often under shade, and is common at Batu Caves, Selangor. It was introduced from Tropical America, probably because of its showy, freely produced flowers, which close in the afternoon.*

Another relative which has been introduced as well, T. subulata grows in sunny places. It has attractive cream-coloured flowers with almost-black centres. It is common around Kuala Lumpur. x 0.4 (FJ,v.1,180)

103 Blechnum orientale *(Blechnaceae). This fern, known variously as* Paku Ikan, Paku Ular *and* Paku Lipan, *is common in sunny and slightly shady places and it will not grow in deep forest shade, unlike most of the ground-fern species in Malaysia, which live in shady wooded areas. The fronds can be up to 1.8m. long, and are only subdivided once. The young shoots can be eaten.*

In the photograph part of a tree fern (Cyathea sp.) can be seen on the left, while the large, arrow-shaped leaves of Alocasia denudata *and the small heart-shaped leaves of a species of* Piper *(Pepper) are visible on the right.* x 0.1 (RFM,v.2,446)

▲102 ▼103

104 **Costus speciosus** (*Zingiberaceae*). *The stems the* **White Costus** *(Setawar) may be 2-3 m. tall, wit spirally arranged leaves, topped by a flowerhead. Th mass of calyxes and associated bracts looks like a littl red pineapple measuring about 10 x 5 cm. One coroll lobe, the pearly-white lip, is greatly enlarged and has yellow base; it forms a platform for the large fema Carpenter Bees which visit it. It is both wild an cultivated in Malaysia and flowers freely all the yea round. (The cultivated form has larger flowers an usually does not set seed.) Unlike many members the Ginger family, the plant has no aromatic smel but contains the steroid diosgenin, which can be use as a raw material in the production of synthetic se hormones. It was used a lot in Malay magical medici and as a neutralizer (setawar) of blood poisoning.*

x 0.3   (FJ,v.3,70

105 **Alpinia javanica** (*Zingiberaceae*). **Grea** **Javanese Alpinia** *(Lengkuang or Tepus Putih) is moderate-sized (3 m. tall) ginger which grows in clump It has the typical ginger growth form with slende curving stem and large elongated leaves arrange alternately on each side. Its leaves are up to 90 cm. lon with fine hairs on the underside. The flowerheads at th top of the stems are typically drooping. It often grow in rather disturbed places. Its spherical green fruit 2.5 cm. in diameter and can be eaten.*

x 0.3   (FJ,v.3,48

106 **Asystasia gangetica** (A. coromandeliana *Acanthaceae). Asystasia* (Akar Ruas-ruas) *is slender-stemmed herb which scrambles upwards whe supported by vegetation. It was introduced from Ind because of its showy flowers, but has run wild. Ther are several genetic variants with pale yellow, whit pink, mauve or violet corollas, and the pale yellow the common 'wild' type.*

The native A. intrusa, with a smaller white coroll bearing a blue patch, is a very common, quick-growing scrambling plant in shady disturbed ground. It form dense growths of brittle, straggling vegetation up 1 m. high if the weak stems are supported, but it very easy to uproot. It is used medicinally by Chines in Pulau Pinang, and there is record of it being use in the Maluku islands, where it was pounded wit onion and lime juice and used to treat dry cough an throat irritation. x 2   (FJ,v.2,576

104▲   105▼

PLANTS OF OPEN SPACES

107 **Arundina graminifolia** *(Orchidaceae)*. *Bam-*
boo Orchid *(or Tapah Weed) shows great variation*
between different populations, but since intermedia
forms occur, they are all lumped together as one specie
It is common on open, disturbed places with poor so
in the lowlands as well as in the mountains. Th
attractive, free-flowering orchid should be cultivat
more. x 0.75 (RFM,v.1,18

108 **Abrus precatorius** *(Papilionaceae)*. **Indian L**
quorice *(Akar Saga) is a twining herb which usual*
grows near the sea. It has clusters of pinkish-mau
pea-flowers and leaves with two rows of up to 20 lea
lets. The photo shows ripe pods with the black-cappe
oval seeds. These were drilled and used as beads. Th
were also used by Indian goldsmiths as weights, eve
though the heaviest seeds were as much as 40% heavi
than the lightest ones. Saga seeds are extremely poi
onous, and there are stories of deaths resulting fro
swallowing drilled seeds. x 1.25 (FJ,v.1,62

109 **Clappertonia ficifolia** *(Honckenya ficifoli*
Tiliaceae). This native of W. Africa was introduced
an ornamental, but has since run wild. Clappertoni
is a shrubby, 2-m.-tall plant with fibrous stems;
belongs to the same family as Jute. x 1 (FJ,v.1,39

107▲ 108▼

110 **Ageratum conyzoides** *(Asteraceae).* **Whi[**
Weed (Rumput Tahi Ayam), *a native of Tropic*
America, is a common ephemeral in open, disturbe
ground in the tropics, and it also grows in the hi[
stations. The flowerheads may be whitish or mauve ar
vary greatly in showiness, and the plant has a
unpleasant smell. In the lowlands the leaves are ofte
attacked by a disease which causes them to crinkle ar
turn yellow.   x 0.67   (FJ,v.2,377

111 **Mimosa pudica** *(Mimosaceae).* **Sensitive Pla[**
(Touch-me-not or Rumput Malu) *is a low, spreadin*
rather wiry plant with hairy stems bearing shar
thorns, as barefoot walkers soon discover. This nati
of Tropical America is now a common pan-tropic
weed. When shaken, the leaflets and leaves droop in
second; recovery takes a few minutes. This is due i
specialized swellings at the base of the moving par
containing cells which leak when physically shocke
Mimosa has been used for treating asthma in t[
Philippines. The root is rich in tannins and was use
for diarrhoea and as a diuretic.   x 0.6   (FJ,v.1,56[

112 **Cassia mimosoides** *(Caesalpiniaceae).* **M[**
mosa-leaved Cassia *has tough, upright stems ar*
tiny leaflets that close at night. It may have bee
introduced but is quite common in undisturbed ope
places. A similar species, but with fewer, larger leafle[
and less showy flowers is known as C. lechenaultian[
                                 x 0.5   (FJ,v.1,53[

113 **Celosia argentea** *(Amaranthaceae).* **Firewee[**
(Bayam Ekor Kucing) *is an upright, 1-m.-tall annue*
with red or green stems and leafstalks, and red or whi[
bracts which colour the flowerheads. It often grows o
the sites of previous fires. This is the wild type fror
which the gaudy plumed and cockscomb forms ar
derived. Cultivated for centuries in China, they are i
demand as pot plants for the Chinese New Year. Th
young shoots can be eaten, and Chinese use the seeds o
a poultice for broken bones.   x 0.4   (FJ,v.1,234

114 **Physalis minima** *(Solanaceae).* **Lesser Bladde**
Cherry (Letup-letup) *is a soft-stemmed, short-live*
herb up to about 50 cm. tall with small, bell-shape
flowers having yellowish corollas and brown-spotte
centres. The fruit is a yellow berry hidden inside th
greatly inflated calyx, which is like a delicate Chines
lantern. Unlike most pan-tropical weeds, it appears i
be a native of the region. Both the Chinese and th
Malays have medicinal uses for the plant.
                                 x 0.4   (FJ,v.2,468

115 **Peperomia pellucida** *(Piperaceae).* **Commo**
Peperomia *is a soft, fleshy-leaved ephemeral of S*
American origin. The frosted appearance of the leave
is due to light reflected from each convex cell wall. I
often grows as a weed in flowerpots, and in cracks i
masonry. It can be eaten raw or cooked, and has
peppery flavour.   x 1   (FJ,v.1,174

110▲   111▼

22 Cardiospermum halicacabum (*Sapindaceae*). *Balloon Vine* (Peria Bulan) *is a pan-tropical weed of open, disturbed places. It climbs by means of tendrils. The fruit is an inflated bladder-like capsule enclosing the round seeds which are 4–5 mm. in diameter. The leaves are edible, while the root has diuretic, emetic and purgative action, and is used in Indian and Chinese medicine.* x 0.5 (FJ,v.2,132)

23 Passiflora foetida (*Passifloraceae*). **Stinking Passionflower** (Timun Dendang) *is a little, pan-tropical herbaceous tendril climber which came from America. The whole plant has an unpleasant smell. The flowerbud and unripe fruit are enclosed in a basket formed from 3 finely subdivided bracts bearing sticky glandular hairs. The shoots can be cooked and eaten, and the pulp of the small, yellow berries is deliciously sweet. The fruit on a plant tend to ripen at the same time, and birds (and children) like to eat them.* x 0.8 (FJ,v.1,290)

▲122 ▼123

124 Hoya coronaria (*Asclepiadaceae*). *This specie[s] is usually found in mangroves or on riverbanks. It is [a] twiner which has thick, leathery leaves with striking hard and fleshy flowers. Unfortunately clusters [of] flowers are produced sparingly. Like other members [of] the Milkweed family,* H. coronaria *produces copiou[s] milky juice.*

There are about 20 species of Hoya *in the Peninsul[a,] most have smaller and more numerous flowers born[e] on stalked clusters.* x 1 (FMP,v.2,40[0])

125 Macrosolen platyphyllus (*Elytranthe platy phylla; Loranthaceae*). *This striking* **Mistletoe** *is [a] semi-parasite found in Peninsular Malaysia, especiall[y] in Negeri Sembilan, and in Peninsular Thailand. It ha[s] ribbed stems, large egg-shaped leaves and cluster[s] bearing few, large flowers.*

Helixanthera coccinea *is another mistletoe foun[d] both in the lowlands and in the highlands of th[e] Peninsula, where it occurs well above the 1,000 [m] contour. It has a large red flower spike with minut[e] white flowers. It sometimes grows on rubber trees.*
x 0.6 (FMP,v.3,15[9])

126 Bauhinia kockiana (*Caesalpiniaceae*). *There [is] a large number of* Bauhinia *species in Malaysia. Mos[t] of them are large, woody climbers which climb b[y] means of tendrils. The flowers vary greatly in size, an[d] the petals, which are yellowish when young, matur[e] to a reddish orange. It is one of the few forest plan[ts] which produces a large showy patch of colour in th[e] forest canopy, and it is sometimes grown in gardens[.]*
x 0.2 (FMP,v.5,30[6])

127 Bauhinia bidentata (*Caesalpiniaceae*). *Ther[e] are quite a few Bauhinias which have been brought int[o] cultivation, including this climbing species. They ma[y] be propagated by cuttings, and some hybrids hav[e] showy flowers. Some* Bauhinia *are trees, for instanc[e] the cultivar* B. blakeana, *or the Hong Kong Orchi[d] Tree.* x 0.[6]

128 Merremia hederacea (*Convolvulaceae*). **Lesse[r] Malayan Bindweed** *is a slender herbaceous twine[r] which is common in open places, often growing as [a] weed. The leaves are very variable in shape, from hear[t] shaped to 3-lobed, and sometimes they have toothe[d] margins. The flowers have short corolla-tubes and d[o] not bear the trumpet-shaped corollas so often found i[n] its relatives.*

A large twining relative, M. peltata *is common i[n] forests and open ground, and can grow to a length [of] 30 m. It has yellow flowers like* M. hederacea, *but wit[h] trumpet-shaped corollas. Its leaves are heart-shape[d] and vary in size from 4–40 cm.* x 0.6 (FJ,v.2,49[0])

The small purplish flowers in the bottom righ[t] hand corner is Cleome rutidosperma *(*Capparaceae[,] a common short-lived plant newly introduced into th[e] region.* (FJ1.183[)]

124▲

125▲ 126▼

▲127 ▼128

129 Dendrobium anosmum (D. superbum; Or chidaceae). *The epithet* anosmum, *Greek for scentles is a misnomer for the flowers smell, to me, like raspberr jam, but with a slightly pungent quality reminiscen of iron filings. It flowers profusely every few month from bare stems, but the flowers do not last long. Th beautiful orchid is now considered 'old-fashioned'. . is a Malaysian native, and there are nearly 100 Der drobium species in the Peninsula.*

x 0.4   (FJ,v.3,374

130 Dendrobium crumenatum (Orchidaceae). Th *commonest flowering epiphyte in Malaysian town: the* **Pigeon Orchid** (Anggerek Merpati) *forms larg clumps on roadside trees. Stems have a spindle-shape swollen and grooved pseudo-bulb near the base, a lor mid-section bearing leaves and, sometimes, a slende knotted, flowering part at the tip. Flowerbuds remar dormant until stimulated to develop by a large fall i temperature due to a rainstorm. The fragrant flower open 9 days later for a few hours only. Hence nearly a the Pigeon Orchids in the area bloom on the same da several times a year. The morning after, the close flowers look like upside-down white pigeons. Unlik most orchid species in the region, the Pigeon Orchi does not hybridize.* x 0.17   (RFM,v.1,8,14,17,329

131 Dendrobium pierardii (Orchidaceae). *This ele gant little epiphyte is rather like* D. anosmum *in habi but smaller. It is found in Selangor and up as far as th Himalayan foothills. It is sometimes brought int cultivation.* x 0.67   (FMP,v.4,51

132 Bulbophyllum lobbii (Orchidaceae). *This 20 cm.-tall orchid comes from the hills, from abou 1,200–1,500 m. altitude. It shows considerable varia tion in form and colour in different parts of its range The plant illustrated is from Sabah. The central hinge lip is so delicately pivoted that when an insect lands o it, the lip tips over and brings the insect into contac with the pollinia (pollen masses). These stick to the hea of the insect and when the process is repeated with an other flower, pollination takes place. This is a difficu plant to cultivate.* x 0.8   (RFM,v.1,421

133 Taeniophyllum obtusum (Orchidaceae). **Leaf less Orchid** *is a tiny epiphyte. The leaves are reduce to brownish scales 1 mm. long covering the singl growing point at the centre of the short stem. Th greater part of the plant consists of thick, flattene green roots which spread out over the bark of its host The flowering stem, 1–2 cm. long, is notched; eac notch marks the position of a fallen flower. Like th Pigeon Orchid, nearly all plants in an area flower o the same day for a single day, but with Taenio phyllum, gregarious flowering occurs at intervals o about 10–20 days. There are 17 species of Taenio phyllum in the Peninsula.* x 8   (RFM,v.1,588

129▲   130▼

▲140　▼141

139

142 **Averrhoa bilimbi** (*Oxalidaceae*). *The flowers* Belimbing Asam *are borne on older branches and on the main trunk. The fruit are very acid and are use cooked or raw, instead of vinegar. They are useful f removing stains on fabric and metal. The pale gree downy leaves have two rows of sensitive leaflets th droop slowly when shaken briskly. Charles Darw grew it is his greenhouse and used it in his studies o motion in plants.*

*Its relative, Starfruit (*A. carambola; *Belimbin* Manis*), has mauve flowers and crisp fruit which tur yellow when ripe and are star-shaped in cross-sectio The fruit have a fresh tart or sweetish flavour. T country of origin for both species is unknown, but th were probably introduced to Malaysia.*

x 0.5   (FT,v.2,2

143 **Etlingera (Nicolaia) elatior** (*Phaeomeria sp ciosa; Zingiberaceae*). **Torch Ginger** (*Kantan*) *is native of Indonesia and Malaysia. It has stems up to m. high of typical ginger growth habit, with stems th bend over towards the light and have elongated leav on both sides. The pyramidal flowerheads are shown i the photograph, and they grow on nearly naked flowerin stems about 1 m. high. The flowerbuds are protected l bracts and the small red tubular flowers with oran; margins are exposed as the bracts open outwards. T outermost bracts are by far the largest. The flowerhe in the 'drumstick' stage (before the flowers are expose is sliced and eaten raw in* rojak, *a raw vegetable sala Ornamental cultivars are sometimes grown, especial in Hawaii.*   x 0.4   (FJ,v.3,6

144 **Mangifera indica** (*Anacardiaceae*). *Several sp cies of* Mangifera *native to Malaysian forests a cultivated, but the best known of these is the* **Mang** (*Mangga*), *which is probably a native of monsoo India. It is rather straggly when young, but matures a splendid tree 30 m. high, with a dense, hemispheric crown. Although the climate is not well suited for it a it is often at the mercy of wood-boring beetle larvae, th tree is popular in suburban gardens. It flowers after dry period, but though it is common for some parts on of the tree to put out new leaves at any particular tin it is rare for it to fruit and flower simultaneously, is seen in the photograph.*

Other native species which are cultivated inclu Binjai (M. caesia), *the strong-smelling* Macang (M foetida), *and, in Borneo,* Bambangan (M. pajang *Rather similar, but with much smaller fruit is t* Setar (Bouea macrophylla).

x 0.17   (FM,v.8,42

142▲   143▼

145 Eugenia malaccensis (Syzygium malaccense; *Myrtaceae*). *Malay Apple* or *Pomerak* (Jambu Merah or Jambu Bol) is a narrow tree, about 15 m. in height, cultivated throughout the region, but it is unknown in the wild state. The leaves are often covered in galls containing larvae of psyllid bugs. It flowers and fruits several times a year. The fruits are whitish green, red or red-streaked, and contain a single large seed. They are quite tasty, but have delicate skins and so are seldom sold in the markets.

x 0.4   (TFM,v.3,247)

146 Eugenia aquea (Syzygium aqueum; *Myrtaceae*). *Water Apple* (Jambu Air) is a small, spreading tree up to 10 m. high, probably of Indian origin. The creamy white flowers have large numbers of showy stamens. The pear-shaped fruit have thin skins and translucent flesh, so appear waxy, but the crispy white flesh is rather tasteless.   x 0.25   (FJ,v.3,247)

147 Passiflora laurifolia (*Passifloraceae*). A slender, woody, S. American passionfruit vine which climbs by tendrils, *Water Lemon* (Buah Susu) has run wild in belukar around towns, but it fruits more freely when growing in full sunlight. The flowers are fragrant and close in the afternoon. The fruit containing numerous black seeds resembles a smooth lemon, but has delicious watery pulp. The laurel-like leaves are poisonous as they contain hydrocyanic acid.   x 1   (FJ,v.1,290)

145▲   146▼

148 Phyllanthus acidus (Cicca acida; *Euphor-biaceae*). *Malay Gooseberry* (Cermai) *is unknown in the wild, but is either Tropical Asian or Brazilian i origin. This 8-m.-tall tree has short leafy twigs, lookin like pinnate leaves, emerging from the tops of the feu thick main branches. These soon fall off, then the re male flowers and pink female flowers appear above th scars of the fallen lateral branches. The fruit is ver sour, and has a single seed. It is used for pickles an flavourings.* x 0.3 (TFM,v.2,122

149 Psophocarpus tetrogonolobus (*Papilion aceae*). *Four-angled Bean* (or Goa Bean) *is unknow in the wild, and is probably of Tropical Asian origin This twining perennial is a prolific producer of roc nodules which contain nitrogen-fixing bacteria, so r may be valuable in promoting soil fertility. It produce pods with 4 soft, jagged-edged ridges, and can do so fo a long time. These pods can be eaten raw or cooked.* x 0.5 (TCD,317

150 Piper nigrum (*Piperaceae*). *A native of the hu mid forests of S. India,* **Pepper** (Lada) *has been trade to China and Europe for over a thousand years. I Malaysia, it is mostly grown in small gardens i Sarawak. Pepper is a root climber, and bears its frui on hanging spikes. Each fruit ripens yellow and turn black when dried. It carries a single seed, which be comes the white pepper when the outer part of th fruit is removed. It contains the alkaloids piperin and piperidine, while its hot taste is due to the resi chavicine. A single seed, or peppercorn, was some times used as a symbolic rent in England — a reli of its great value in the medieval times.*

The Betel vine, P. betle (Sireh), is a similar aro matic plant which rarely, if ever, flowers in Malaysia The leaves are chewed with areca nut, slaked lime gambier and tobacco. x 0.5 (FJ,v.1,170

151 Theobroma cacao (*Sterculiaceae*). *In the pre Columbian days in Tropical America,* **Cocoa** *wa believed to be of divine origin and had great value. Thi 5-m.-tall treelet probably evolved on the eastern slope of the equatorial Andes. It grows at low altitudes in th humid tropics, preferably under light shade. The pod are harvested when the seeds begin to rattle. The seed are allowed to ferment for about a week. This kills th seeds and destroys the tannins, and leads to th development of the characteristic taste and colour.*

The illustration is of an old-fashioned cultivar Cocoa cultivated in Malaysia nowadays has pods whic are green, turning yellow as they ripen. x 0.8 (TCD,571

148▲

149▲   150▼

152 **Ceiba pentandra** *(Bombacaceae). The* Kap*
(or Kekabu) tree came from Tropical America, wh*
it is a large forest tree. It grows up to 18 m. tall, and h
green-barked, horizontal branches which come off *
blunt-spined, straight, grey trunk in groups. T
deciduous leaves have many radiating leaflets, wh
the off-white, bat-pollinated flowers smell of sour mi
The wind-borne seeds are supported by air-filled fib
which repel water and are used for stuffing pillows a
for insulation. Unripe fruit and the seed oil are edib
It is an important crop in Java. x 0.1 (FJ,v.1,41

153 **Cocos nucifera** *(Arecaceae). The place of orig*
of the very useful **Coconut** *(Kelapa or Nyor) has lo*
been controversial. However recent findings by Harr
of self-sowed wild-type coconut palms in the Philippin
and N. Australia seem to have settled the matter.

In the picture two female and numerous male flo
ers, borne on spikes which have burst out of the sheat
ing spathe, can be seen. x 0.17 (TCM,44

154 **Areca catecu** *(Arecaceae). The* **Areca Pal**
(Pokok Pinang) is a 10 m. tall, slender palm grown f
its hard, nut-like seeds which contain the alkaloid ar
coline. The nut is strongly astringent as it has up
25% of catechol tannins. This is the 'nut' in the bet
nut quid. It grinds down and polishes the teeth, a
thereby provides some protection against tooth deca
x 0.1 (FJ,v.3,19

152▲ 153▼

*e typical of wind-pollinated flowers. The young shoots
*n be cooked and eaten. In New Guinea, each tribe has
*s own special cultivar of this and they use it to mark
ie boundaries of their fields.　　　　　　 (HT,291)

This species should not be confused with the true
Croton (Croton tiglium), *whose seeds contain croton
*l, a blistering agent which is the most drastic purga-
ve known.　　　　　　x 0.4　　(FJ,v.1,493)

63 Cordyline terminalis *(C. fruticosa; Aga-
aceae). The wild **Ti Plant** (Andong) has green leaves
*hich are used to make leaf skirts in the Pacific as they
*o not shrivel. There are several cultivars which differ
*i leaf colour. Other cultivars have smaller or more
*ensely packed leaves. These and the purple-leaved
*ultivar in the picture are grown for ornamental foliage.
*he plant flowers rarely, and Chinese consider its
owering a sign of good luck.*　　　x 0.3　　(FJ,v.3,160)

64 Graptophyllum pictum *(Acanthaceae). Prob-
-bly a native of E. Indonesia and New Guinea, the
aricature Plant (Puding) may reach a height of
*m. Several cultivars with differently-coloured leaves
*re grown. Flowers are few, and always the same
*olour. It is the food plant of the caterpillars of the
utumn Leaf Butterfly, Doleschallia bisaltide.*
　　　　　　x 0.67　　(FJ,v.2,579)

▲163　▼164

151

165 Gardenia jasminoides (G. florida; *Rubiaceae*
A native of S. China, the **Gardenia** (Bunga Cina)
a shrub 3 m. high. The double-flowered cultivar, pr
pagated by cuttings, and the form with variegate
leaves are common. The flower has a rich "tropica
scent, but it soon turns black in the centre and peta
become pale yellow. It is particularly susceptible
mealy bugs. Its dried corollas are used to flavour te
x 0.8   (FJ,v.2,31

166 Ixora javanica (*Rubiaceae*). **Javanese Ixo**
(Pecah Periuk) is a 3-m.-high shrub with show
inflorescences. It is native to Malaysia, and there a
about 20 species in the Peninsula. The paired leaves a
pale green, up to 20 cm. long and tend to hang dow
Flowers open orange-red and turn red later.
x 0.75   (FJ,v.2,32

167 Clerodendrum paniculatum (*Verbenaceae*
Pagoda Flower (Sepangil) is about 3 m. high, slight
branched and woody-based. Its dark, shiny, 3-lobe
leaves have an unpleasant smell, while the conic
flowerhead comprises numerous small red flowers.
is very attractive to the spectacular Birdwing an
Swallowtail butterflies, possibly because of the colo
of the flowers. It is probably native to SE Asia and the
are 17 species in Peninsular Malaysia alone. It w
used in Malay magic to summon spirits.
x 0.6   (FJ,v.2,60

165▲   166▼

168 **Orthosiphon aristatus** *(O. stamineus; Lam‑*
aceae). **Cat's Whiskers** *(Kumis Kucing) is a native*
SE Asia. This herb grows about 75 cm. high. It has
long corolla-tube from which projects the 5-cm.-lon
style and the slightly shorter stamens. The stem, an
the leaves, may be purplish. The Chinese use Orth
siphon *to treat diabetes.* x 0.67 (FM,v.8,380

169 **Crinum asiaticum** *(Amaryllidaceae). The hug*
handsome **Crinum Lily** *(Poison Lily or Bakong) me*
grow up to 1.5 m., and is native to SE Asia. It
commonly grown in gardens and can take a lot
maltreatment. It has an underground bulb and low
parts of the leaves form stout pseudo-stems. Flowe
are delightfully scented. Large types, like the o
pictured here, grow wild in freshwater or brackis
swamps, while smaller types grow on dry, san
seashores. They are poisonous, and are used
traditional medicine. x 0.3 (FJ,v.3,13

170 **Hibiscus rosa-sinensis** *(Malvaceae). It seen*
fitting to end the book with Malaysia's National Flowe
the **Red Hibiscus** *(Shoe Flower or Bunga Raya).*
native of East Asia, where the pink, white and yello
forms have long been cultivated, it has been grown
Malaysia for hundreds of years. It is easily grown fro
cuttings, and many beautiful cultivars have be
developed. The leaves are edible and may be used
an emollient. x 1 (FJ,v.1,43

168▲ 169▼

GLOSSARY

aroid:	A member of the Arum family (Araceae).
axil:	The upper angle between stem and leaf, a common site of origin of buds or roots.
berry:	A juicy fruit with numerous seeds embedded in pulp.
bract:	A leaf-like structure below a flower or flowerhead.
bulb:	A much shortened stem bearing fleshy leaf bases or scale leaves (e.g. onion).
calyx:	The outer envelope of a flower, consisting of separate sepals or fused calyx-lobes, typically green.
corolla:	The inner envelope of a flower, consisting of separate petals or fused corolla-lobes, typically not green.
cultivar:	(*abbr.* cv.) A variety of plant which originated in cultivation and maintains its characteristics when propagated.
double-flowered:	A flower with an increased number of petals; often the other floral parts are underdeveloped.
family:	A group of one or more genera which share certain common characteristics (e.g. Moraceae, the Mulberry family includes the genera *Morus*, the Mulberries, *Ficus*, the figs, and *Artocarpus*).
genus:	(*plural* genera) A group consisting of one or more species which share certain common characteristics (e.g. *Artocarpus* includes the three species: Breadfruit, Jackfruit and Cempedak).
herb:	A plant with a soft, non-woody stem (herbaceous plant).
hybrid:	The progeny of parents of different genetic constitutions.
latex:	A milky juice, often containing rubber, found in certain plants.
leaflet:	The individual parts of a compound leaf.
node:	A joint in a stem from which leaves, and sometimes roots, arise.
pinnate leaf:	A compound leaf divided once, twice or thrice into leaflets.
pistil:	The female part of a flower, consisting of the ovary at the base, and the (sometimes) elongated style tipped by the stigma.
rhizome:	An underground stem bearing buds (e.g. ginger).
sepal:	One of the outer series of sterile leaf-like organs of a flower, usually green; a constituent part of the calyx.
shrub:	A woody plant which branches at ground level, typically with more than one stem.
spathe:	A large bract enclosing a flowerhead (e.g. in Aroids and Palms).
species:	(*abbr.* sp.; *plural* spp.) A group of individuals which can interbreed. Because of their common ancestry they share a set of heritable characteristics which distinguish them from other species.
spike:	A flowerhead bearing stalkless flowers on a single axis.
ssp.	Abbreviation for subspecies.
stamen:	The male part of a flower, consisting of the (usually yellow) anther, which produces pollen grains, and the threadlike filament, which supports it.
tree:	A large woody plant with a single main stem.
variety:	(*abbr.* var.) A naturally occuring subdivision of a species.

BIBLIOGRAPHY

Floras: *These scholarly books aim to deal with all members of certain plant groups growing in a defined area.*

Flora of Java, 3 vols., C.A. BACKER and Bakhuizen VAN DER BRINK. (1963–8) Noordhoff, Groningen. 2140 pp. Describes most wild and cultivated plants in Malaysia.

The Flora of the Malay Peninsula, 5 vols., H.N. RIDLEY. (1922–5) L. Reeve, Ashford. Comprehensive, but now somewhat out of date.

Flora Malesiana, ed. C.G.G.J. VAN STEENIS, various authors. Series 1, Flowering plants, v.1 (1950)–v.9 (1983). The definitive Flora (partly completed) of the region encompassing Brunei Darussalam, Indonesia, Malaysia, the Philippines, Singapore and New Guinea. Some species illustrated by line drawings.

Flora of Thailand, eds. Tem SMETINAND and Kai LARSEN, numerous authors. Until v.3 (1979) ASRT Press, Bangkok. A definitive Flora, of which only a small part has been completed. Partly illustrated by line drawings.

A Revised Flora of Malaya, 3 vols.: v.1 Orchids, R.E. HOLTTUM—2nd ed. (1973), v.2 Ferns, R.E. HOLTTUM—2nd ed. (1968), v.3 Grasses, H.B. GILLILAND (1971). Government Printing Office, Singapore. Partly illustrated.

Tree Flora of Malaya, vols. 1–2, ed. T.C. WHITMORE, v.3, ed. F.S.P. NG. (1972–) Longman, Kuala Lumpur. A forest Flora of native trees excluding Dipterocarps, to be completed by vol. 4.

Other references:

Hortus Third (1976) Macmillan, New York. 1290 pp. A concise dictionary of plants cultivated in the United States and Canada, covering over 20,000 species and cultivars.

Kinabalu: Summit of Borneo (1978) Sabah Society, Kota Kinabalu. 482 pp. Highlights the plant life of Gunung Kinabalu in over 140 pages of text and illustrations.

ALLEN, B.M., *Malayan Fruits* (1967) Donald Moore Press, Singapore. 246 pp.

CORNER, E.J.H., *Wayside Trees of Malaya*, 2 vols. 3rd ed. (1988) Malayan Nature Society, Kuala Lumpur. 861 pp. A classic work with 236 black-and-white plates.

FOO Tok Shiew, *A Guide to the Wildflowers of Singapore* (1985) Singapore Science Centre. 160 pp. Fully illustrated account of 82 species, mainly common Malaysian weeds not described in this book.

HENDERSON, M.R., *Malayan Wildflowers*, 2 vols. (1954) Malayan Nature Society, Kuala Lumpur. 835 pp. Mostly descriptions of herbs, with 625 line drawings.

HOLTTUM, R.E., *Plant Life in Malaya*, 1st paperback ed. (1977) Longman Malaysia. 254 pp.

POLUNIN, I. *Plants and Flowers of Singapore* (1987) Times Editions, Singapore. 160 pp. Companion volume to this book, concentrating on urban vegetation and plants introduced to the region. 200 colour plates.

PURSGLOVE, J.W., *Tropical Crops Dicotyledons* (1974) Longman. 719 pp. *Tropical Crops Monocotyledons* (1975) Longman. 607 pp.

WEE Yeow Chin and R. CORLETT, *The City and the Forest: Plant life in urban Singapore* (1986) Singapore University Press, Singapore. 186 pp.

WHITMORE, T.C. *Palms of Malaysia*, rev. ed. (1977) Oxford University Press, Kuala Lumpur and Singapore. 132 pp.

WHITMORE, T.C., *An Introduction to Tropical Rain Forests* (1990), Clarendon Press, Oxford.

YONG Hoi-Sen, *Magnificent Plants* (1981) Tropical Press, Kuala Lumpur. A beautifully photographed picture book of Malaysian plants.

INDEX OF SCIENTIFIC NAMES OF PLANTS

159

ACKNOWLEDGEMENTS

It is a pleasure to acknowledge the help of friends. Many of them have gone out of their way to help me by reading and commenting on my drafts, checking and confirming the identities of various species, and all this within record time.

Among the many people who have made it possible for me to write this book, I would particularly like to thank the following:

Encik Ali Ibrahim, Singapore Botanical Gardens
Dr John Dransfield, Royal Botanic Gardens, Kew, England
Dr Hsuan Keng, Department of Botany, National University of Singapore
Dr Ruth Kiew, Universiti Pertanian Malaysia
Puan Anthea Lamb (nee Phillipps)
Encik Tony Lamb, Agricultural Department, Sabah
Datuk Lim Chong Keat, Pulau Pinang
Encik James Maxwell, School of Pharmacy, Chiang Mai University, Thailand
Haji Mohd Shah, Singapore Botanical Gardens
Dr Benjamin Stone, Academy of Natural Sciences of Philadelphia, U.S.A.
Encik Jason Weintraub, Department of Entomology, Cornell University, U.S.A.
Dr Tim Whitmore, Department of Plant Sciences, Oxford University, England

PHOTO CREDITS